FOREWORD

In editing the text, and checking the illustrations, I have been struck most by the wealth of information assembled in this series. For thirty years I have made a wide study of the animal kingdom, and while much of this information was already known to me, I was constantly coming upon an interesting fact or story which was entirely new to me. It is hoped therefore that readers of these volumes will be similarly entertained and informed.

Some of these stories struck me as so remarkable that I thought they must be untrue, yet, when I checked them, I found they were correct; or as correct as our knowledge takes us to the present day. For in dealing with animals you never know when knowledge that is accepted today may not be proven wrong tomorrow. One other thing that impressed me, as I searched the books and the libraries, or went to museums and zoos to check the details, or talked with scientists having special knowledge of particular animals, was that, in spite of the wealth of books on the subject, much of what is known about animals is inaccessible to all but the favoured few. The chief value of these books, therefore, is that so much information, otherwise scattered, and often difficult to obtain, has been brought together in a highly interesting form, and illustrated with vivid coloured drawings.

HUNTERS OF THE ANIMAL WORLD

BIRDS, FISH AND AMPHIBIANS

EDITED BY

MAURICE BURTON, D.Sc.

ODHAMS BOOKS LIMITED

LONG ACRE, LONDON

INTRODUCTION

In this, one of three volumes entitled THE HUNTERS, that deal with the hunting animals of the world, we are concerned primarily with the sea and the sky, with the finned and winged animals that hunt along their unseen currents. Also included are the stories of the hunting amphibians, those animals that can live both on land and in the water. The ancestors of all these animals originally evolved as hunters, but many of their modern descendants have developed new and specialized skills.

The first fish of which we have fossil records differed from more ancient sea life in its possession of an internal skeleton and an armour of bony scales. But it was the evolution of an archaic jaw and the development of paired fins that first enabled fish to pursue and capture their prey. Thus equipped for the hunt, fish went on to occupy all the world's waters and ultimately to out-number all other vertebrate forms of life, even the millions of birds that crowd the skies.

Birds came much later in the evolutionary story. The first bird of which we have knowledge dates back only one hundred and fifty million years, whereas fish were already swarming through the ancient seas more than four hundred and twenty-five million years ago. Not until the first fish had crawled out onto the land, had given rise to the first amphibian and later given rise to the first reptile, was the stage set for birds to venture into the skies, empty until then except for insects.

The amphibians have continued their primitive way of life largely unchanged. Although they have not developed the far-sighted eyes of the soaring hawk or the lethal electric charge of the ocean-dwelling ray, they are among the most fascinating of the world's hunting animals.

PREMEDITATED MURDER

Hurtling at one hundred and ten miles per hour from the skies, the **lammergeyer** almost knocks the chamois off its four sturdy legs. Quickly the chamois spins to face its attacker, but before it can regain its footing the persistent predator delivers other stunning blows that drive it back, relentlessly, until confused by terror, the chamois takes the last, fatal step, and plummets to its death on the rocks below. In triumph, the majestic lammergeyer glides in graceful circles, watching carefully for any tell-tale signs of life, for despite its ten-foot wing-span and vicious hooked bill, the lammergeyer is not normally a killer. Had the chamois fought back, this canary in hawk's clothing would no doubt have turned tail and fled, for it is easily frightened and incapable of defending itself against animals half its size. This timorous character always checks to be certain its prey is dead before cautiously approaching the body, and rarely, if ever, has been known to kill by direct attack. Its main food is bone marrow, small bones being swallowed whole, larger bones being dropped from a height onto rocks to crack them. A lammergeyer will crack open a tortoise in the same way.

When we start to look more closely into the ways of the animal hunter we soon get the impression, with many of them, that there is something cowardly in their natures. Perhaps if this were not so the species they prey upon would soon be wiped out and they themselves would perish. Certainly what has been said of the lammergeyer and the chamois could be said of many others, that if the prey only stood its ground and fought back the hunter would, in many instances, retreat. It has even been seen for a mouse, being chased by a cat, to turn on its attacker in a fury causing the cat to run.

Lammergeyer (*Gypaetus barbatus*)

7

Andean condor *(Vultur gryphus)*

LORD OF THE ANDES

Fit inhabitant of the majestic mountain ranges of the South American Andes, the **Andean condor** is monarch of all it surveys. Largest of all flying birds, its body is a full four feet long, and the wing-span often exceeds ten feet. It roosts in trees during the heat of the day, being most active in the early morning and evening. Then, from its favourite look-outs on inaccessible rocky ledges, it surveys all below with a telescopic sharpness of vision. On sight of a victim, any small mammal, goat, lamb or fawn, it streaks out of the sun like a diving fighter-plane. Its terrible talons strike with killing force and pluck the prey from the ground. Mostly, however, the condor feeds on carrion, for death is ever busy in the mountains, and provides many a carcass for scavengers to consume. A gluttonous feeder, the Andean condor gorges itself until sleepy with repletion. In this state hunters can climb after it and lassoo it before it is fully active.

Comparing the condor with a fighter plane is much more appropriate than might appear. One of the problems associated with airfields and with aeroplanes actually in flight is the presence of birds. They tend to come into collision with the machines or, in the case of jet planes become sucked into the engines. The condor is an even greater menace. It has been known deliberately to attack aircraft daring to invade its air-space.

HIS MAJESTY THE EAGLE

The **golden eagle,** a symbol of power and freedom and sometimes called the sovereign of the celestial firmament, is fierce and proud. Strong and agile, with a wing-span of eight feet, it can lift its own weight which ranges from eight to twelve pounds. Legend has it that a golden eagle has carried a lamb for five miles and has also kidnapped small children. A hunter by trade, and rapacious by instinct it lives on grouse, hares, rabbits and other small animals. Outside the breeding season the bird is solitary. Although found throughout the Northern Hemisphere, you would have to climb the highest and craggiest peak to find its humble abode. Pugnacious and tenacious it has almost

Now a married woman, she keeps the torn frock she then wore as a souvenir of one of the world's most amazing adventures. As it is the habit of eagles to kill their prey before bringing it to the nest, Svenhild's escape must be one of the most extraordinary on record. The golden eagle is reputed to be a menace to shepherds in mountain pastures, who have to be on the alert wherever young lambs or goat kids are apt to stray. When baulked of its prey it may possibly turn on the animals' protector.

THE BALD EAGLE

If the hard work and skill of the raccoon should cause it to be elevated to the status of the American National Emblem in place of the carrion-feeding **bald eagle** this move would please a great number of people. For although this eagle has great natural ability as a hunter, it prefers to take its food in other ways. It

Golden eagle (*Aquila chrysaetos*)

Golden eagle (*Aquila chrysaetos*)

been drowned on occasions when it has gone fishing and refused to let go of a giant pike.

EAGLE AND CHILD

Stories are often told of eagles carrying off a lamb or child, but real-life instances capable of proof are very few. It is generally agreed by ornithologists that an eagle is unable to carry a weight in excess of its own, and few of these birds weigh more than twelve pounds. However, there seems no reason to doubt the terrifying experience of four-year-old Svenhild Hansen, who was actually "kidnapped" by an eagle near Trondheim in Norway in June, 1932. She was playing in the yard of her parents' farmhouse when an eagle swooped down on her, fortunately clutching only her dress in its talons. The giant bird is then said to have carried her "more than a mile" towards its eyrie. Becoming tired, it deposited her on a ledge eight hundred feet up on a mountain and fifty feet short of the nest. Only the fact that the eagle was seen to fly repeatedly over the spot gave a clue to the panic-stricken parents and a party of searchers. Eventually little Svenhild was found there fast asleep, uninjured except for slight bruising and a few scratches.

feeds largely on fish, especially dead fish lying on the shore. It will also harry an osprey carrying a fish, pouncing until it forces its quarry to drop its catch, and then promptly catching the fish before it reaches the ground. If the osprey cannot give the eagle the meal it has waited so patiently for, then it may itself become the victim. The bald eagle's diet is mainly fish and birds, although it will attack and kill animals the size of young deer. It nests in treetops, and once established will return to the same place year after year.

Benjamin Franklin was well aware of the doubtful character of this bird of prey when he spoke of it as "a bird of bad moral character... who does not get his living honestly". He reinforced this remark by saying further that "like those among men who live by sharping and robbing this eagle is generally poor and often lousy." A natural question, is why such an unattractive bird should have been chosen as the symbol of freedom and the other ideals for which the Americans had fought.

For two-and-a-half thousand years at least the eagle has been used as a symbol of sovereignty and nobility. It was natural, therefore, that the

Bald eagle (*Haliaeetus leucocephalus*)

newly-independent American nation should look to this kind of bird as a national emblem. But they had to find an eagle native to their country and also one that was not found elsewhere. The only eagle to fulfil these two conditions was the bald-headed eagle.

In common with so many birds of prey the bald eagle has been persecuted until there came a fear that the national emblem of the United States might become extinct in real life. In 1940 the National Emblem Law was passed banning the killing of the bald eagle. This law, however, was not extended to Alaska where the bird existed in large numbers along the coast and on the adjacent islands, where the fisheries and fur industries formed so large a part of the economy of that region. While it is true that the bald eagle eats fish, much of this is already dead and the reason, so we are told, why the bird

Ornate hawk-eagle (*Spizaetus ornatus*)

was persecuted in Alaska was because of its habit of perching on the poles of the fish traps. This caused the salmon caught in the nets to panic, to beat against the nets and so damage themselves that they were spoilt for canning. In addition there were fox farms on many of the small islands and for obvious reasons of economy the foxes were allowed to roam freely. The bald eagle sometimes killed these.

Over 100,000 eagles were killed before simple remedies were suggested. One was to put a spike on each pole of the fish traps, which prevented the eagles from perching there. The other was to restrict the movements of the foxes and to cover their compounds with screens that hid them from the eagles.

DEADLY PURPOSE IN HIS BEAUTY

Ornate, which means ornamental, is an apt description of this most distinctively-marked bird of prey. The bright neck and cheeks, short crest and graceful poise of the head, add together to make an unforgettable image of beauty combined with perfectly controlled power. The **ornate hawk-eagle** in flight, especially when "braking" a descent, with wings, tail and talons all contributing to the decisive moment of a strike, is a picture of terrible efficiency devoted to the supreme purpose of killing to live. It inhabits the northern shoulders of the South American continent, parts of Central America, and districts of southern Mexico. In fact, wherever plains and open stretches interrupt the dense tropical jungle. In length it averages about twenty-four inches and feeds largely on reptiles, particularly green lizards and snakes, although it will also take birds on the wing, hovering high, then zooming down to extinguish life with a single blow of its immense, hooked talons. A fearsome example of beauty hiding a deadly purpose.

BATELEUR EAGLE WITH IMPALA DOE

This colourful bird has a wide range of hunting territory, for it is found in nearly all parts of Africa south of the Sahara. Very short-tailed for an eagle, it makes up for this by the wide span and immense strength of its wings, and it is often seen at considerable heights flying at speed. Its diet varies according to the district it inhabits. Occasionally it descends to feed on carrion, but nearly always prefers to do its own killing. This is especially so where large herds of antelope roam the wilds with their young.

13

Bateleur eagle *(Terathopius ecaudatus)*

The **bateleur** fixes on some unlucky little antelope lamb temporarily strayed from its parents, and streaks through the air like a projectile from a gun, the wind whistling through its feathers with a noise like that of a shell zooming to its target. The lamb simply hasn't a chance. The frightful impact and bone-crushing clench of the eagle's claws kills at a stroke, and the lamb is then carried to the eyrie to be devoured at leisure.

MAGNIFICENT EAGLE

Majesty, poise, plumage and power have earned the adjective "Magnificent" for the **white-tailed sea-eagle.** The length of the female from beak to tail-tip averages about thirty-eight inches, the male being four to five inches shorter. This is the only eagle of this kind to be met with in the British Isles, and then only rarely in recent years, although a century ago it was common there. However, it is still wide-spread in most temperate or northerly climates from Europe to India and Japan. In addition to its while tail it sports a

White-tailed sea-eagle *(Haliaeetus albicilla)*

brown waistcoat and wing coverts, but the thing you will notice most is the form of its beak. It projects straight forward for most of its length, then curves smoothly down into a deeply curved hook. This serves for the quick and efficient carving up of fish, mammals and anything else the eagle can bring to its nest. Although labelled a sea eagle, it raids the land too.

EAGLE VERSUS KANGAROO

A big fellow is the Australian **wedge-tailed eagle,** over three-feet long, needing plenty of nourishment to give power to the beat of its great wings. What better meat than the tender flesh of a young kangaroo browsing away from its mother's side! Down plummets the eagle, streaking from the blue with talons outspread, but mother kangaroo has stamped an urgent warning on the earth. Her baby makes a frantic long hop and a convulsive leap into the safety of the maternal pouch, while the disappointed eagle has to check its darting dive at the last split-second and zoom past in savage frustration.

Australian wedge-tailed eagle *(Aquila audax)*

Red-tailed hawk *(Buteo jamaicensis)*

African crested eagle *(Lophoaetus occipitalis)*

WINGED NEMESIS

High in the cloudless blue sky, a **red-tailed hawk** circles slowly. Suddenly, its sharp eyes spy the dark shadow of a prairie dog against the flatland hundreds of feet below. Immediately, the handsome bird noses over into a steep dive, gaining speed like a falling rock, its wings pinned back against its streamlined sides. As it nears the ground, the hawk flattens out into a shallow glide, aiming itself straight at the unsuspecting target. At the very last second it spreads the great wings, which cuts its speed like an airplane's dive brakes, and it drops its "landing gear". The surprised prairie dog, alerted too late, has barely time to turn its head before the talons snatch it up and carry it to a high ledge where the red-tailed killer devours it. One of a number of winged predators whose beauty graces the skies of the Americas, the red-tailed hawk can be seen waging its aerial warfare on man's rodent enemies from Alaska to Panama.

PLACID BUT DEADLY

When squatting, with only its dark upper plumage showing, and its long crest ruffled by a breeze, this African hawk-eagle looks like a black cockatoo with a lot of worries. Actually it is a quiet, seemingly contemplative bird, often seen sitting silently among the tree-tops in open, partially-wooded districts from the Nile to South Africa. But the moment it sees something eatable below, it is after it like a flash, uttering shrill cries which its victims have hardly had time to hear, because the eagle is on them so swiftly. Snakes, lizards, rats and mice, ground squirrels, frogs and small birds are included in its diet. The eagle's nest is neither so large nor so untidy as that of other birds of prey, being a neat affair of sticks in a tree-fork, lined with green leaves. Often it is close to nests of biting ants who share the same tree, but the ants never attack the **crested eagle**. It is as though they knew the bird to be a quiet and well-behaved neighbour.

FRESHWATER FISHERMAN

Except in the southern hemisphere and in Ceylon, the **Pallas' eagle** is a common sight in the Far East, but to classify it as a Sea Eagle is a mistake. It lives mostly in open country beside marshes or rivers, and feeds on fish, aquatic birds and, in some parts of India, on turtles which it regards as a great delicacy, especially before their carapaces, or shells, have reached the hardness of maturity. It is not so speedy in the air as most eagles, owing to the heavy structure of its wings. Nevertheless, its wing-span enables it to hover and to select at leisure any fish that may be basking at or near the surface of pool or river. In times of scarcity, or when its eaglets are squawking urgently for food, it will not hesitate to pick up carrion, as vultures do, and carry the odorous carcase meat to its nest.

Peter Simon Pallas, after whom this eagle is named, was born in Berlin in 1741. He studied medicine and later became a professor of natural history in St. Petersburg, at the invitation of the Empress Catherine. He is famous for his expeditions into Asia to study its natural history.

Pallas' fishing eagle (*Haliaeetus leucoryphus*)

Harpy eagle (*Harpia harpyja*)

TYRANT OF THE TREE-TOPS

Where tree-tops form a leafy canopy over the steaming jungles of South and Central America lives the **harpy eagle,** which has the strongest talons of its tribe. This bird differs from all others in its way of life, for it hunts monkeys, sloths, birds, lizards and all tree-dwelling creatures, not from the sky above, but actually within the forest canopy itself. With its short, immensely strong pinions the harpy eagle can wheel and dart at an amazing speed, dodging the stems and branches of trees in its relentless pursuit. It can turn over in mid-flight to snatch some poor cowering animal that may have vainly sought refuge underneath a branch. Only occasionally will it descend to a clearing and hunt at ground level.

The harpy eagle was worshipped by the warriors of the Mayan peoples of Central America centuries ago.

Osprey or fish hawk *(Pandion haliaetus)*

FISHERMAN WITHOUT TACKLE

This winged angler is one of the most widely distributed birds in the world. Its diet, consisting almost entirely of fish, ensures that it is never found far from water. A fearless hunter, the **osprey's** technique is to soar in circles until it spots its prey, then to streamline its body by half-closing its wings, and plunge down with legs stretched in front and talons spread. Often it goes completely underwater only to reappear a few moments later, grasping a fish. Indeed it has even been seen diving into surf in which no human could survive. Every now and then, a prowling eagle, watching the ease with which the osprey catches its prey and finding it more convenient to force a tribute rather than hunt for itself, will chase the angler. Eventually the fish hawk surrenders its booty. But with its family waiting in the large nest on the top of the tree for their "daily bread" this competent fisherman must return to its task, and will not return empty-handed even if it means catching only a frog or an eel.

A few years ago an osprey, in North America, was seen to stoop at a large fish in a lake. The osprey drove its talons into the fish and was in danger of being dragged under by it. The bird saved itself by spreading its wings and then, by flapping its wings, it paddled itself to the shore. Once in shallow water it was able to drag the fish on land where it renewed its grip and tried to fly away with its prey. The fish was too heavy for this and after a few ineffectual efforts to take off it ate half the fish and flew away with the rest. The man who reported this incident was struck by what he thought was the great cleverness of the osprey, first in saving itself from drowning by spreading its wings, then by paddling ashore, and finally, and this he thought the cleverest part of the performance, eating half of it to reduce the load it had to carry.

This story is not so remarkable as it appears at first. To begin with, the immediate instinctive action of any bird faced with circumstances that cause it alarm or put it in danger is to spread its wings. For a bird on land this is a natural preliminary to taking flight, and followed by a thrust of the legs, makes the bird airborne. This would explain the osprey spreading its wings in the first place. The second instictive action of any bird having spread its wings would be to beat them. This would normally result in flight, but in the case of the osprey in question the wings acted as paddles and carried it to the shore.

18

Swallow-tailed kite (*Elanoides forficatus*)

ACE FLIER

This truly beautiful bird, most graceful of fliers, grows to a length of two feet, and is easily identified by its long forked tail. It inhabits chiefly open forest lands from North Carolina to Mexico and Florida, and spends most of its active time floating high in the air, with only an occasional beat of the wings. Its wonderfully keen sight enables it to dart down a hundred feet or more to pick an insect out of the air. From the ground it takes snakes, lizards, frogs and smaller animals which it snatches up from the earth with scarcely an interruption in its flight. Small mammals or other birds are seldom taken if other food is available. The **swallow-tailed kite** usually hunts alone, but it has been known to join in a flock in order to pursue a swarm of bees. Its nest may contain 2 or 3 eggs, and is built high up in the fork of a tall pine or cypress.

The swallow-tailed kite is also found in South America. In many parts of North America, where it used to be plentiful, it has been wiped out. The causes are two-fold. Its beautifully marked eggs have been much coveted by collectors. Added to this the kite defends its nest making it vulnerable to the gun.

MEANEST OF THE FALCON FAMILY

Along the highways that cut through the mountains and valleys of Central and South America, numerous birds of prey have discovered that man's automobiles have made their work easier. Each day, they can be seen patrolling the long ribbons of asphalt and concrete, searching with hungry eyes for the regular toll of dead animals left by speeding cars. One of the most aggressive of these "highway patrolmen" is the **red-throated caracara**. This cousin of the proud and beautiful hunting falcons often grows to 22 inches long, and sports a naked red face and throat on top of its black and white body that makes it resemble its ghoulish consorts, the vultures. Mean-tempered and belligerent, it will fight with these very vultures for the rights to a freshly-killed carcass, often managing to drive them away to look elsewhere for suitable booty. It makes its nest on the ground, spurning the heights where other falcons are found, and stays down below where it can find easy pickings.

The natural diet of the caracara includes insects, among them bees and wasps, the bird plundering their nests, ignoring the angry buzzing of their owners.

19

Red-throated caracara (*Daptrius americanus*)

BINOCULAR EYES

Hovering, apparently motionless, at a fair height from the ground, the graceful **common buzzard** searches for small mammals and reptiles. When its eyes, as powerful as bino-

Common buzzard (*Buteo buteo*)

it is not always easy to recognize from its plumage alone, for colour in this species is very variable, some individuals being dark, others almost white, with many shades in between these. As is usual in hawks and harriers the female is the larger. Both male and female build the nest, in a tree or on a rocky ledge, making a platform of sticks. Here the young are born blind and helpless. Both parents feed the young, which cannot stand until three weeks old.

A buzzard in flight gives an impression of leisurely movement, when soaring with spread wings, but it is said to be among the fastest birds when diving. It has great braking power in checking its descent. When hurtling down at 100 miles per hour it uses "wing flaps" for last minute split-second control more effectively than any device yet invented for a flying machine.

Goshawk (*Accipiter gentilis*)

BEWARE OF HIS CLAWS

A vice-like grip of the talons is the killing weapon of the European **goshawk**. When attacking a bird in flight, a single crushing clutch from one foot is enough to deal swift death. Unlike other birds-of-prey, the goshawk does not let its capture fall to the ground, but "rides" its prey to earth to feed on it at leisure, landing in a sheltered spot where it can get a good view all around. If disturbed it will always return to its kill. Its main prey are low-flying, heavy-bodied birds such as ptarmigan or grouse, but it may snatch at a finch or a tit. Its usual habit is, however, to go ground-hunting for hares, rabbits, squirrels, even unfortunate fowls that have strayed from a farmyard. More high-flying game is left to the female goshawk, for she is bigger and more powerful than the male, and may attack birds larger than herself, with talons whose grip is even more tenacious than that of her mate.

culars, have spotted something moving it drops to earth in an easy swoop. As it makes a "hit" its sharp talons hold the victim to the ground giving the hooked bill the chance to administer the coup-de-grâce. Ranging from the forests and fields of Sweden to the sunny islands off Spain, the common buzzard is the most numerous of the buzzards. Nevertheless,

power diving at lightning speed and literally impaling its victim with a deadly thrust of the hind talon. Game birds are its favourite food, but it also takes smaller birds and will also kill hares and rabbits on the ground with the same regal ruthlessness. Compared to its regal cousin, the tiny **red-thighed falconet** is a toy-sized killer.

THE WINGED VIKING

Like its close relative the Iceland falcon, the **gyrfalcon** has been, for centuries, prized as a sporting bird, and is still valued as such, especially in the United States. It is found throughout the more northerly parts of the Northern Hemisphere. In its native haunts it feeds more sumptuously than any captive fed by man. The treeless marshy plains of Norway and Lapland, in particular, offer it an abundance of grouse and wading-birds, and it also takes larger birds, such as geese. Pictured here is a gyrfalcon in the act of killing a heron. Despite its size and strength the heron is helpless in the clutch of its enemy's talons, although the death struggle may continue for half-an-hour with the gyrfalcon never relaxing its grip. The female gyrfalcon, as though conscious of her

Gyrfalcon (*Falco rusticolus*)

Iceland falcon (*Falco rusticolus islandus*)
Red-thighed falconet (*Microhierax caerulescens*)

THE ROYAL HUNTER

Falconry, as the prized sport of emperors, kings, sultans and sheiks, has a history of more than two thousand years, first in China, then Arabia, then in Europe during the Middle Ages. Four hundred years ago the Knights of Saint John of Jerusalem "rented" the Island of Malta from Spain, paying a tribute of one falcon per year. The **Iceland falcon** seen here is also known as the gyrfalcon, of which it is a subspecies, both being proud descendants of a long line of royal hawking birds. After being set at a bird the falcon will rise high before

21

power, makes no nest, but lays her eggs on the bare ground, usually on a cliff-top overlooking a valley or an inlet of the sea, at most supplying a few sticks and moss, or else she takes over the disused nest of a larger bird.

HIGH FLIGHT, HIGH SPIRIT

A bird of the falcon family with cousins all over the world, except in Australasia, is the perky foot-long **American sparrow hawk** found all the way from northern Canada to Tierra del Fuego. Although well known for its cocksure air and spirited way of flying, it does not often fly after sparrows or other small birds and thus is not well named. It might better be called a rodent hawk, for mice and other small rodents are its favourite food, together with insects, as with its relative in Europe, the kestrel. The American sparrow hawk will turn into the wind and hover until it spots a movement down below. Then it glides steeply down and another meal has been nailed to the ground. The female American sparrow hawk lays four or five eggs in a clutch, generally in a nest of her own, but occasionally in the abandoned nest of another bird. As she helps her mate to

Peregrine falcon

(*Falco peregrinus*)

American sparrow hawk (*Falco sparverius*)

rid fields and hedgerows of many a pest, these falcons can be reckoned as creatures that are good to have around.

Like the peregrine the American sparrow hawk kills swiftly and surely, using its notched beak to take a secure grip on the larger of its prey.

ROYAL COMPANION

Even before the Pyramids were built in Egypt, Arab lords of the desert trained **peregrine falcons** for hunting. In the Middle Ages European monarchs made "falconry" a royal sport, especially in England, where kings allowed their earls to use the peregrine. In this sport the birds were flown like arrows from the

Merlin (*Falco columbarius aesalon*)

padded glove of the falconer, but in the wild state the peregrine loves to zoom sky-high before hurtling down on his prey. Then comes the shock of impact when dagger-sharp talons stab deep into the victim with the force of a snapping steel trap. A spray of blood and a whirl of feathers or fur show the violence of the strike. In flight the peregrine kills ducks, game-birds, or anything that attracts it; or it can dive to the ground like a falling bomb on rodents or other small animals. The falcon is perhaps the world's swiftest flier, for observers say it can speed up to two hundred miles per hour, a figure that is largely guesswork, yet it is small in proportion to its power; about fifteen inches long, with a thirty-inch wing-span. Today, it is the mascot of the Jordan Arab Legion, the soldiers of which have adopted it, as their ancestors did thousands of years ago.

Most birds never exceed 60 miles per hour and many do not fly at more than 40 miles per hour. Even the peregrine can only reach this high speed when diving on its prey.

THE MARK OF THE HUNTER

In mediaeval times, falcons were status symbols denoting the rank of the hunters. Only royalty could fly the large gyrfalcon, earls only the peregrine, and to the hunting clergy the little **merlin** was assigned. Though not as powerful as the other falcons, the merlin is still a formidable predator. Despite its eleven-inch size, it is audacious enough to catch young rabbits, young partridges and rock doves and to reward its owner with an afternoon of exciting sport. The merlin has been clocked at a speed of about fifty miles an hour, that is much faster than its usual prey, such as meadow-pipit, skylark and linnet, and it can also dart with agile swiftness to strike the little scrambling vole. The art of Falconry is still practised although less in vogue than formerly, and a young merlin when caught and trained can become quite an entertaining pet.

In England the merlin was used for what used to be the popular sport of lark-hawking. It is surprising to find that this was not prohibited until the Bird Protection Act of 1954.

Red-thighed falconet (*Microhierax caerulescens*)

Secretary bird (*Sagittarius serpentarius*)

PRIDE OF BLOOD

In Asia there lives a proud and aristocratic little bird about the size of a sparrow, the smallest of that high and noble family of hunters, the Falcons. Proud of spirit and as daring as its larger cousins, it reproduces their appearance in miniature in every detail. It is called the **red-thighed falconet.** Because of its modest size it hunts mainly insects, but its proud connection with the noble breed of falcons is seen when it attacks birds and animals larger than itself. Its thighs are covered with "trousers" of red feathers which distinguish its family from any lower and unworthy lineage. It rests high up, in the cavities of dying trees, and with the dead wings of insects carpeting the inside of its roost. Upon this soft, unusual mattress the female lays her eggs.

The falconets sit in pairs on dead branches occasionally flying out to seize an insect or they may fly in small circles catching and eating insects on the wing. They will also fly out at small birds.

SPINDLE-LEGGED SNAKE-HUNTER

When the **secretary bird** comes calling, even the deadliest snake had better hide, for this odd-looking creature is a master of the fine art of killing snakes. Found throughout the African grasslands from the Egyptian Sudan to Cape Province, the secretary gets its name from the crest of long feathers that look like old-fashioned quill pens stuck behind its ears. Most of its four-foot height is taken up with the long, gangling legs that allow it to walk faster than a man can run. When it spies a snake, it approaches, weaving and flapping its wings. By confusing the aim of the reptile's fangs, it can pin the writhing serpent with one powerful foot. Then, seizing its victim behind the head, it either dashes it to death or takes it aloft and kills it by dropping it from a great height to the hard ground below. When no snakes are handy, it fills out its diet with rodents, lizards and insects, which it finds living in great abundance on the hot, dry veldt.

THE DEMON LOVER

A snore, several coughs, a hoot, a whistle, then wild, crazy laughter – these are the love calls of the **barred owl.** Noisy in courtship, it is quiet in flight, for, as with all owls, its feathers are equipped with delicate filaments that enable it to hunt its prey in silence. With eyes looking straight ahead, with ears that can accurately pin-point the slightest rustle, and with a set of sharp, strong claws it is ready for its victims. Being twenty inches high, it is big enough to kill with ease smaller owls, as well as other birds, squirrels and snakes as it hunts during the darkest nights. It nests in the hollows of trees throughout the woodlands of Central America, Mexico, and the eastern United States. Courageous in defending their nests, the barred owls nevertheless seem to invite their enemies, as they strew their homes with the heads and wings of their prey, leaving tell-tale "tracks" for their own foes to follow.

The barred owl is one of the species used by American scientists twenty years ago to test which senses were most used for hunting at night. Their tests show that hearing alone enabled them to pounce on a mouse moving among dried leaves in complete darkness. Equally interesting was the information obtained about the use of sight. The owls were able to detect objects at night when the light-intensity was up to one-hundredth of that we require to see things in the blackness of night.

Barred owl *(Strix varia)*

THE MOANS OF AN EVIL SPIRIT

Many prowlers haunt the depths of South African forests, and mysterious nocturnal noises give rise to strange legends and superstitions among the native tribes. The weirdest sound of all is that made by the **milky eagle owl,** that flits like a ghost through the twilight gloom and in the dead of night. Though its wings are silent, its voice is noisy, for it utters frightening cries, loud and mournful, suggestive of an evil spirit suffering torments of agony or despair. However, it is in the nature of owls to hoot, and to call to each other. The milky eagle owl grows to a length of about 2 feet, and its appearance is solemn and impressive, with tufts over its ears which look like horns. Hence

Milky eagle owl *(Bubo lacteus)*

Great horned owl (*Bubo virginianus*)

Snowy owl (*Nyctea scandiaca*) ➡

its claim to kinship with the Horned Owls. Its hearing is acute, matching the sight of its great eyes, so that it hunts as much by ear as by vision. No small forest-dweller is safe when the milky eagle owl is hungry, but as rats and snakes figure on its menu its prowling is useful to man.

DEATH IN THE SNOW

On the fringes of the Arctic and in the subarctic playground of his cousin the **snowy owl,** the somewhat darker **great horned owl,** of North America shrieks his maniacal, spine-chilling call that sends a tremor through all within ear-shot. After hearing one of these "mating calls", it is small wonder that for centuries the owl has

been associated with witchcraft and occult evil. Both the snowy owl and the great horned owl stand more than two feet high and both are very skilful hunters. While the great horned owl pounces on grouse, squirrels, skunks and rodents that abound in the forest, the splended white snowy owl glides over icy wastelands on silent wings, searching mainly for lemmings. When these are scarce it will take almost any prey, such as arctic hare or ptarmigan, and will attack arctic foxes caught in traps. Streaking down with hawk-like speed, this beautiful but deadly bird sinks its powerful claws into its victims and carries them off to devour at leisure. When the lemming "crop" is abundant, the female snowy owl will lay up

to thirteen eggs, but when food is scarce, she will not even make a nest, and she and her mate will join the great horned owl in migrating as far south as Texas.

NIGHT HUNTER

Unaware that an enemy with exceptionally keen ears is lurking in the trees above, listening to its every movement, a mouse rustles through a European forest searching for food. Before he can enjoy his dinner, the **tawny owl** swoops down through the night air, kills the struggling rodent, and soars off with it securely held in its sharp, hooked bill. The tawny owl is more strongly nocturnal than most owls, but if it ventures in daylight, or even stays out after dawn, there will be a sudden riot as finches, thrushes, starlings and other small birds gather round it to harass it with their noisy, excited chorus. This is poetic justice for the tawny owl often preys on these same birds and their young when it has the chance. An audacious spirit with a powerful pounce, this "wise guy" of the skies will even strike birds and animals larger than itself when aroused.

THE PIXIES

Being eight inches in length, the **little owl** is well named, for stripped of its feathers it is no larger than a starling. This is one of the surprising features of owls: how small the body is under the feathers. Found in many European countries, the little owl is usually seen by day perched upon a post, although it hunts by day and by night. Germany, Holland and England

Tawny owl (*Strix aluco*)

are some of its more northerly homelands, but its real centre of distribution is the sunny countries that border the Mediterranean. Despite its small size, this owl takes small birds and

1. Saw-whet owl (*Aegolius acadicus*)

2. Little owl (*Athene noctua*)

mammals, but it takes many insects in addition. However, a little owl has been known to consume five mice in a single meal. The **saw-whet** is the little owl of the New World. From Mexico to Alaska these birds can be seen roosting together, in an evergreen tree or the hollow of a decayed trunk.

THE DESERT ELF

The miniature **elf owl**, five and a half inches long, is found in the southwestern United States and Mexico. Although sometimes living among pines or oaks near the coast, it is more commonly found in open desert spaces, in small crevices or in a hollow in a cactus. It lives solely on insects which it hunts by night,

Elf owl (*Micrathene whitneyi*)

THE TERROR OF THE BROOKS

Patiently waiting upon a stump or overhanging bough, the **European kingfisher** scans the stream for a passing minnow. When sighted, the bird flashes down into the water like a streak of lightning. If it comes up to the surface "emptybilled", it may well try its other method of fishing, for the blue and chestnut kingfisher will hover above the water, then plunge like a plummet from a height up to thirty feet upon a swimming prey. Its food is two-thirds fish, with a fair quantity of aquatic insects, and it will also take water-snails, frogs, and worms. Widely distributed over much of Europe and north-west Asia, this seven-inch bird nests not far from streams and lakes. Kingfishers make an eight-foot horizontal tunnel in a bank, with the nesting chamber at the end. The nestlings are fed in an unusual way. When a parent arrives with food, the nestlings see its shadow and move round one, so that each is fed in turn.

RACKET-TAILED KINGFISHER

Flying from perch to perch, the **racket-tailed kingfisher** hunts the floor of wet forests of New Guinea and the Moluccas looking for centipedes and lizards. It will often sit like a statue with only its tail twitching quietly, waiting for its prey to show itself. As soon as it sights something it swoops down and will often drive its bill into the muddy earth to effect a capture. The plumage of the racket-tailed kingfisher is considered to be the most resplendent of any kingfisher. It is a

European kingfisher (*Alcedo atthis*)

both on the ground and in the air. Its marvellously sensitive hearing and huge eyes, well adapted to "seeing in the dark", enable it to swoop on them with unerring aim. During the day it sleeps in the shade for its eyes cannot stand the blaze of the desert sun. For one so small, it has a surprisingly loud voice, giving out a succession of whines, barks, and yelps resembling the cries of a puppy.

An elf owl roosting in a cactus furnishes an interesting example of the interdependence of animals. The hollow it uses is not natural but is a cavity chiselled in the cactus by the gila woodpecker in which to lay its eggs. When the woodpecker family has fledged and departed the owl takes it over.

slender, scarlet-billed bird, about fourteen inches in length, and its most conspicuous features are narrow, flagged central tail-feathers.

This is one of a group known as tree kingfishers that in their habits have departed from what we usually expect of kingfishers. They either fly out from a perch to catch insects on the wing, like flycatchers, or swoop on prey on the ground in the manner of the butcher birds.

Racket-tailed kingfisher

(Tanysiptera galatea)

FOUR OF A KIND

About eighty species of kingfisher live in various corners of the world. The most primitive species are woodland birds that spend the day diving down on to insects, lizards, and small rodents from their perches in the trees. The more advanced species are fish-catching acrobats, famous for their headlong plunges into rivers and streams.

One of the largest of the aquatic species is the **blue crested American kingfisher.** Motionless on its exposed perch overhanging the freshwater streams and lakes of North America, it watches for minnows in the water, then drops like a stone to seize one in its sharp-edged beak. Back on its perch, it juggles its catch so that it can swallow it head-first.

The world's smallest fisherman, the **Malay forest kingfisher** lives deep in the forests of Malaysia and Indonesia. Not more than five inches long, it clings with its three-toed claws to its perch in the familiar upright stance of its larger kingfisher relatives – watching for small fish and frogs, crustaceans, newts and water insects. Ten species of these bright-billed jewel-like little birds flash above the streams in these tropical forests.

A migratory bird, the **Cape kingfisher** ranges from the Cape Verde Islands across the open bush country of southern Africa. Nesting along the banks of streams and rivers, it feeds only on land insects, frogs and small lizards. Content to follow the old order, the Cape kingfisher scorns the aquatic acrobatics of its fish-diving relatives, and observes the time-honoured ways of the ancestral kingfishers.

Another primitive species, the **pigmy kingfisher,** darts along the tree-shaded roads of the grasslands south of the Sahara. Like its water-feeding relatives, it digs a typical kingfisher tunnel into an ant-hill or soft bank of earth. Despite its size, it is so rapid and quick that it can often catch insects on the wing, making up in agility what it lacks in body-size.

LAUGHING DOWN UNDER

Going home to roost in the tree-tops, the flock of **kookaburras** sends forth wild peals of crazy laughter. Not so funny, however, for the Australian who wants to sleep, for these birds are so punctual in their morning chorus that they are known as the bushman's clock. Although the seventeen-inch kookaburra is considered to be a kingfisher, it is not restricted to well-watered regions. Its laughter can be

1. **Blue crested American kingfisher** (*Megaceryle alcyon*)
2. **Malay forest kingfisher** (*Ceyx rudiforsum*)
3. **Cape kingfisher** (*Halcyon leucocephala*)
4. **Pigmy kingfisher** (*Ispidina picta*)

introduced European starling for nesting sites in the gum trees that remain.

The felling of a gum tree a few years ago brought to light an interesting piece of natural history. A man walking through the bush stopped to talk to two foresters clearing the land. He was surprised to see two kookaburras return to an imaginary spot in the air, about twelve feet up from the ground, hover for a few seconds and then fly away. He drew the attention of the foresters to this and they assured him that the birds had been doing this for a couple of days. They then added that there had been a kookaburra nest in a tree which they had pulled down on that spot. We often speak with a certain amount of wonderment about swallows returning in spring, after an absence of six months or more, from South Africa 6000 miles away, to the same barn or stable, even to nest on the same rafter. The direction taken by the swallows is, we know, determined by the sun. When the birds arrive at their destination they must also be influenced by land marks, by the gross features of the landscape and the smaller details of the barn. The two kookaburras flying up to a nest that was no longer there is a very clear indication that birds do carry the memory of features of the landscape, but it goes further, for the immediate surroundings had been quite altered. So for the kookaburras to have been able to fly up into space, where the nest used to be, they would seem to have been relying on the more distant features of the landscape for their bearings.

Kookaburra (*Dacelo gigas*)

heard in coastal bushlands, thinly timbered forests and even the drier plains. In all these areas its most dramatic flight is with a wriggling snake caught in its broad bill. High up in the air it will let the reptile drop – to certain death, and then pick it up, dead, to eat. A lizard, on the other hand, is whisked away to a branch, where its head is battered before the meal begins. In perhaps this same tree the female builds her nest. If any intruder should approach the home, both big-billed adults will dart down hard. To try stealing their pearl-white eggs is no laughing matter.

It is a sad thought that the numbers of the kookaburra may be threatened because so many gum trees are being felled in Australia. This is inevitable as civilisation and human settlement advance and it is made worse by the kookaburra having to compete with the

Woodchat shrike *(Lanius senator)*

THE HANGING LARDER

Size is no object when the **woodchat shrike** is stocking its larder. This eight-inch bird, of Europe, perches on a branch, post or other look-out point, flying from there to the attack when prey presents itself. It kills, not with talons, but with hammer-blows of its beak. A peculiar habit of the shrike is to impale insects, lizards, mice and shrews on thorns of a bush, making the area around look like a ghoulish above-ground cemetery. Some of this impaled food may be eaten immediately, but most of it is left hanging for future use. The rest, for no apparent reason, is completely ignored.

Nobody knows whether this is a method of storing food for future use or not. Very few birds make any attempt to hoard food, and it is more likely that to credit the woodchat shrike with this much foresight is to take the wrong view. So far as one can see from watching them at work, the woodchat shrikes find it easier to despatch their victims by impaling them on thorns or barbed wire, or by wedging them in a fork of a branch. One argument that can be used against the idea of the woodchat shrike hoarding food against future use is that it is only a summer visitor to Europe. It spends the rest of the year in Africa, and this period is the summer in the southern hemisphere. Therefore, not only does the bird leave Europe even before food is becoming scarce but it migrates to its winter quarters where food is still abundant.

It is so easy to misinterpret the actions of animals, and another example of this is seen when woodchat shrikes mob a fox that comes near their store of small carcases. They are not doing this to keep the fox away from their stores. They would mob a fox wherever they met it, just as other small birds will mob a fox or, more commonly, an owl.

THE PETTY TYRANT

A nine-inch bundle of feathered ferocity is how the **kingbird** could be rightly described. Crowned with a hidden cap of orange feathers that flash "danger" when it is angry, the little tyrant will attack anything that trespasses on its territory, even large birds-of-prey. Brooking no intrusion in its nesting area, the kingbird will harass birds many times its size with such audacity and fury that the interloper invariably turns tail and zooms off as fast as he can go. Not satisfied merely to rout the offending party, the kingbird will continue its onslaught until the trespasser is far, far away. Because of its aggressiveness Indians, east of the Mississippi, pay it homage and call it "Little Chief". Having a "sweet tooth" as large as its

Kingbird *(Tyrannus tyrannus)*

Helmet or wood shrike *(Euryceros prevosti)*

courage, it will also attack beehives, grandly ignoring the buzzing madding crowd around.

FIGHTERS ALL

"All shrikes are bullies, aggressive and blood-thirsty", says a distinguished naturalist, and the habits of the African **helmet** or **wood shrike** would seem to confirm this statement. But like other creatures, including man, it must eat to live, and fight for its living. We hear of shrikes seizing helpless young birds and pecking out their brains to provide a tasty morsel, whilst ignoring the rest of the body. Yet its chief food consists of fruit, insects, and perhaps centipedes and small lizards. A fascinating feature of its nest is that its grassy fibres are most ingeniously bound together with spiders'

webs. In many districts shrikes band together in companies to protect their nesting grounds. Fortified by numbers they become exceedingly daring, and will even mob and "dive buzz" an invader as large and formidable as a leopard. When feeding, the helmet shrike's movements are so quick through the trees, picking up food as it goes, that hunters on foot cannot keep pace with it. In every way it is a bird of strong character.

THE FLYING BUTCHER

Wedged in the crotch of a tree, a dazed and wriggling lizard awaits execution. Although sorely wounded it struggles for its life, but the **grey butcher-bird** devours it. This eleven-inch predator with its scaled "booted" legs and black feathered mask looks every inch the executioner it is. As soon as it sees its prey, be it lizard or a bird like the honey-creeper, it wings down from its perch, strikes it a stunning blow with its hooked beak, and, before its victim can regain consciousness, impales it on a sharp thorn or a jagged-edged broken branch. Strangely enough, at this point the butcher-bird may feast on the dead animal, or may leave it hanging there, either to devour it at a later date, or to let it shrivel and dry, completely forgotten. Widespread throughout Australia, the butcher-bird is known for its clear, mellow voice, which it uses to sing antiphonal love duets with its mate.

Ground hornbill
(*Bucorvus leadbeateri*)

Grey butcher-bird (*Lanius excubitor*)

USE AND ORNAMENT

With slow deliberate walk, neck undulating forward at each step, the **ground hornbill** surveys the ground ahead with is unwinking eyes. At intervals it utters loud cries like "Bu-oo; bu-oo". A snake crosses its path. In an instant it has jumped on it, stabbing it to death with its pick-axe beak, its wings beating time. There is a quick flip of the head, and the dead snake is tossed into the air, to fall straight into the hornbill's wide open mouth, to be

swallowed at a gulp. It is the same with other reptiles, molluscs, and rats. Up they go, and down they go! When full of food the ground hornbill flies up into the trees. In many parts of tropical Africa this bird has one very special use. It eats garbage and carrion as eagerly as vultures do, so it is much valued as a part-time scavenger. But it can be ornamental as well as useful. The picture shows the hornbill as a mascot of the Fourth Nigerian Regiment.

Ground hornbill (*Bucorvus leadbeateri*)

Toucans (*Ramphastidae* sp.)

THE MACABRE WAR DANCE

With much flurry and fanfare, the **ground hornbills** perform their tribal war dance spelling eventual death to the central character – a nine-foot mamba snake. Using their wings as shields, each in turn tempts the reptile into striking harmlessly on its trailing wing feathers whilst the others rapidly peck away at the snake's exposed neck and spine. Around and around they go, until the mamba makes one last exhausted lunge. Instantly, the hornbills jump on it, trampling it to death and tearing its body into pieces. Although credited with having a sense of humour, these birds are more mischievous and cruel. They enjoy making veritable pests of themselves to other birds and mammals, particularly to monkeys. A native of Africa, this four-foot, turkey-like bird delights in catching small bats, teasing them, tossing them into the air, and catching them with a self-satisfied gulp. Regarded as a tribal fetish, the **ground hornbill** lives unmolested by the Africans who will, on occasion, tame it. It differs from other hornbills in many ways. For example, the female is not sealed in her nest.

ARTFUL DODGER

One would think that with their bright colouring of red, yellow, blue, black and orange, **toucans** would be very easy to spot in the lush

New Guinea cassowary (*Casuarius casuarius*)

green foliage of the Amazon forests. But this is not so. The toucans live among flowering trees or heavily-laden fruit trees where their gaudy plumage blends into the multi-coloured background. They are robbers and assassins, preying on lizards and small reptiles looking for insects, killing and eating them before the little victims even see their attackers. The frog flipping its tongue at a mosquito is fair game for this hidden aggressor. If a toucan cannot kill the small bird it is chasing, it will often attack the nest, stealing the eggs or taking the young. In some species of this "nosey" bird, the bill is almost as long and bulky as the body. Yet, it is very light, for inside it is porous, like plastic foam, and the shell-like covering is very thin but very strong. Otherwise, with such a large bill it would be taking a nose-dive every time it tried to fly.

Kea *(Nestor notabilis)*

NEW GUINEA CASSOWARY

The native was returning home late in the evening humming to himself, when in front of him he heard a curious howling, grunting noise. An instant later a shape hurled itself upon him. Two slashing claws raked down his body, he fell backwards, and his attacker trampled over him and rushed on. He was very lucky, for he had met a **cassowary,** a notoriously bad-tempered bird, almost five and a half feet tall, out hunting for food. Although in the dense forests of New Guinea and Australia cassowaries feed mainly on berries and plants, they will sometimes kill small animals for meat. They fight by hurling themselves at an opponent, slashing downwards with their powerful claws, which will kill a man. On its forehead the cassowary has a bony helmet which protects it as it runs through the thick under-

growth at a speed sometimes reaching almost thirty miles an hour. It can also swim rivers but will do so only in an emergency.

THE MURDERING PARROT

This exceptionally sharp-beaked member of the parrot family has a very bad reputation. Found only in New Zealand, the **kea** passes the summer high in the mountains of South Island, feeding mainly on fruit but also taking insects and worms. But when winter comes it descends to the plains where sheep-farming is one of the main activities. It is there that this otherwise harmless vegetarian changes character. Originally its ancestors pecked the sheepskins hanging outside sheep stations for insects, or tasted offal from the slaughter-houses. Later generations of keas, having acquired this taste for flesh, began to prey on the bodies of living sheep, chiefly for the sake of the kidney-fat they had learned to look for. So expert is the kea that it will alight on the back of a sheep exactly where the kidneys are most easily exposed. The cruel beak finds its meal in an instant, leaving the poor beast mortally wounded.

STATELY SNAKE KILLER OF THE PAMPAS

A familiar figure on the pampas of Brazil, Paraguay and the Argentine is the stately **crested seriema.** Three feet in height when full-grown, this crane-like bird is one of several descendants of huge carnivorous birds that stalked the Americas and Europe during the Eocene period, fifty million years ago. One of these, the *Diatryma steini,* stood seven feet tall and had a bill shaped like a hatchet. Time, however, has taken its toll on both size and ferocity, and now the crested seriema lives mainly on a diet of fruit, berries, insects, and large ants. Some of the old ferocity remains, though, in its attitude towards the lizards and snakes that abound in its homeland, in the way it runs them down and kills them with its sharp claws and beak. The seriema is easily tamed, and the local peoples keep it around their homes to protect them from poisonous reptiles.

THE FLIGHTLESS RAIDER

About the size of a chicken, this native of New Zealand cannot fly despite the fact that it possesses a pair of well-developed wings. Highly valued in the past for its oil, it was hunted ruthlessly by the Maoris until it was nearly exterminated. Consequently the **weka** is a rare sight today. Sleeping by day in nests under the buttress roots of large trees, this swift ground-bird ventures out only at night to stalk rats, mice, and other small mammals, as well as ground-nesting birds, even those as large as a duck. Grasping its prey firmly with its sharp claws, it can deliver devastating death blows with its powerful beak. Bold and adaptable, this bird has been known to sneak into

Crested seriema *(Cariama cristata)*

Weka *(Gallirallus australis)*

houses and make off with brightly-coloured trinkets. Stealing away into the night, the weka will pause with its mate, from time to time, to sing a shrill piping duet.

RARE AND RAPACIOUS

The beautifully coloured **takahe** has always been a rare bird. Indeed, during the whole of the 19th century only four were ever found, the last supposedly being killed in 1898. After 1900 the species was classified as "possibly extinct" but in 1948, in an isolated valley of New Zealand, it was rediscovered. Now, even with the Dominion government protecting it, the little colony of thirty to one hundred takahes faces possible extinction. This strong-legged bird is flightless in spite of a wingspan of three feet; and though it can kill a duck in fair combat and out-distance a chicken, it cannot always outrun the frequent bush fires or escape the clutches of hungry weasels. Severe winters also take their toll for the mountain snows submerge its normal diet of sedge and snow grass. Perhaps the most dangerous factor in the takahe's fight for survival, however, is infertility, for fully forty per cent of the eggs laid do not hatch. Clearly, if any one of these dangers markedly increases, the strik-

ing blue-green takahe will join the ranks of the dodo and the great auk as another creature lost to the world forever.

FAST, FEATHERED RUNNER

Asleep in the blazing heat the Mexican boy is not conscious of the mortal combat between his half-tamed protector, the **roadrunner,** and a deadly rattlesnake. The odds are on the bird, for though it usually feeds on smaller animals,

Takahe *(Notornis hochstetteri)*

When upright, trumpeting its loud whooping call, it stands nearly five-feet high. But mostly it hunches its shoulders and its great beak is held low, ready to dart at snakes, small alligators or shellfish. These are swiftly stabbed to death by this powerful weapon, which can also neatly pick up frogs, worms or other delicacies to be swallowed whole. More tricky is the "finger-tip" precision of its beak in catching insects for its young, though these soon learn to fend for themselves. They are able to leave the nest for short scrambles the day they are born. Unfortunately, however, for the survival of the species, only two eggs are laid in a year, and a lot of accidents can happen to eggs! So, what with slow breeding and man's interference with their habitat, they are gradually dying out. Observers say that no more than thirty whooping cranes now migrate each year to southern Texas.

THE DAINTY DEMOISELLE

Standing to the left of the whooping cranes is the dainty **demoiselle,** the smallest of the cranes. With its long black neck plumes, and the whisp of white feathers behind its eyes, it is a handsome bird indeed. It breeds in the

1. **Demoiselle crane** (*Anthropoides virgo*)
2. **Whooping crane** (*Grus americana*)

Roadrunner (*Geococcyx californianus*)

it seems to regard rattlers as its greatest enemies. It belongs to the family of American ground-cuckoos. Unlike other cuckoos they do not lay their eggs in other birds' nests but build their own and, as a schoolboy once said, "lay their own eggs!" The roadrunner is a husky bird, about twenty inches long, and it actually does run along roads and tracks as well as in and out of brushwood. It can run fast but not very far, nor do its weak wings allow long-distance flights. For all that it is a keen and determined hunter, using its strong beak as a dagger to kill its prey. By this means it accounts for many noxious insects and venomous reptiles that infest the sun-parched areas of the American continent.

TALL AND DIGNIFIED

Among the rare birds that conservationists are trying to save from extinction is the dignified **whooping crane,** the tallest of American birds.

marshes of the River Danube delta or in southern Spain, but some individuals fly north in the summer as far as Denmark and Sweden. The demoiselle cranes winter in southern Asia and north-east Africa. Their migrations may go on both day and night, the birds flying high in V-formation, only gliding when they are about to land. The journey's end is usually a grassy marsh. Here they will use their strong bills to dig out their diet of roots, worms, insects – even snakes, from the soft earth. The demoiselle crane's bill is also its drinking glass. After pushing this long instrument below the water's surface, it rears its head up high – then swallows.

THE TALL TALL CRANE

One of the tallest birds in the world lives along the rivers and in the paddyfields of India, Burma, Thailand and the Philippines. Here the 5-foot high **sarus crane** has avoided the near extinction that a few of its relatives have suffered in North America. Since many Asian people consider it bad luck to kill a crane, this one walks and flies without fear and is found even near the towns. Moreover, it kills off many pests such as snakes, rodents and insects, and so is regarded as a friend. Although easily tamed, the sarus crane has a fierce streak in it; its long beak can become a stabbing sword if anyone approaches its hidden nest. The male is so devoted to his mate that it is said he will die of a broken heart if she is killed. Male and

Sarus crane (*Grus antigone*)

female share the incubation of the eggs. When the young hatch they can walk about almost immediately. Four months later they learn to fly; it is only after their second birthday, however, that they acquire the plumage of their parents.

A HARD LIFE

The majestic looking bird, flying with slow but powerful beats of its wings, feet trailing behind, neck shaped like a capital "S", was unaware of the descending hawk until they collided in an explosion of feathers. The **common heron** fell, spinning to the ground dazed but unhurt. Nursing its injured dignity, the heron stalked off to the nearest marsh where it remained foraging. Like a flash, it dipped its long beak into the water, withdrew it, tossed a silvery fish into the air, caught and swallowed it in a single gulp. After resting on one leg, the common heron slowly made its way to another spot. A fox chose this moment to attack from the flank, but defending itself

Common heron (*Ardea cinerea*)

with savage and fierce stabs from its long sharp beak, the heron drove the fox away, and continued its slow walk through the marshes.

GREAT BLUE HERON

Nesting in colonies, occasionally with other species, usually building its large stick nests in trees fifty to one hundred feet from the ground, the **great blue heron** is a distinctive and well-known bird, found mainly in North America and the West Indies. The flight of the heron is stately, for the wings are long and wide, and it moves through the air in dignified yet swift flight. Its long beak, sharp and dagger-like, can be used with great force. When attacked, or aroused, the heron's instinc-

Great blue heron (*Ardea herodias*)

tive reaction is to strike at the eyes of its enemy. When out hunting, it will stand on the water's edge, as still as a statue, its head resting between its shoulders. If a fish should swim by, its neck uncurls and the heron strikes down into the water with the speed of a cobra. It also likes a change of diet at times, and mice, rats, small birds, all fall prey to this beautiful blue-tinted bird.

THE BOAT-BILLED HERON

Hidden in the mangrove thickets, along the rivers, marshes, and swamps of South America,

Boat-billed heron (*Cochlearius cochlearius*)

lives a curious bird, the **boat-billed heron.** A frog-like croaking, an indistinct squawk, a muffled bark, a clapping and rattling of a bill, a faint splash in the water, as another fish meets its fate, is probably all that can be heard or seen of this bird. Its broad scoop-like bill is two to three inches long, and two inches wide, but so strangely formed that it resembles two boats one inverted on top of the other. Sitting on branches in the swamps, this heron fishes in a

Great white heron (*Egretta álba*)

way similar to the kingfisher. Watching the fish below, it will dive straight in, pounce on a fish, scoop it up in its bill, and swallow it whole. The boat-bill, whose upper parts are largely grey, with black patches on its head, sides and back, is a very shy bird. A night hunter, during the day it is almost impossible to see, with the result that little is known of its habits.

THE WHITE KNIGHT

Its elegance makes the **great white heron** an eyecatcher in any country. The beautiful bird is found not only in Europe but in America as well, especially in the marshes and swamps. Its food is insects and fish, snakes and lizards. In the evening when the hunt is over it will leave the ground for its roost away up in the trees. It flies high in wide, wonderful circles in the air. Up in these boughs, never far from the sea, the handsome male and his "lady fair" pay court to each other. Later, in June, the light-blue eggs hatch. The little ones, even before learning to fly, will congregate with as many as twenty other youngsters. When these reach adulthood, their snowy trains will be long enough to conceal their tails. This bit of beauty caused their mass slaughter in many areas, for years ago officers and nobles bought these feathers to bob above their helmets. Against the plunder of its plumes the heron's sharp six-inch bill was its only defence.

POMPOUS SCAVENGER

When India was under British rule, a regular visitor to army parade grounds was a stork whose pompous way of walking earned it the name of Adjutant. Today it is better known by its African name, the **marabou**. There are three species: one in India, one in south-east Asia and one, that shown here, in Central Africa. It is attracted to slaughter houses, garbage dumps, and wherever offal is carelessly thrown, for it is an enthusiastic scavenger. Indeed it is so useful in native streets and villages that it has become almost a "citizen" protected by law. The marabou not only gets rid of decaying flesh, but many dangerous snakes and reptiles which it swallows whole. It has even been said to kill and swallow fully-grown domestic cats, the only bird able to do so. Moreover, the marabou often drives away vultures and gorges itself on the carrion they have found. The skinny pouch hanging from its throat is a kind of wattle, usually flabby, but sometimes blown up like a balloon. It is believed that this serves in some way the bird's breathing, but nothing definite is known about it. One thing it certainly does do is to make the marabou's ungainly appearance even less attractive.

The nickname Adjutant came more easily because the marabou is as tall as a man.

THE CASE OF THE STILT-LEGGED KILLER

Deep in the tropical forests of Central Africa, the tall 52-inch **saddle-billed stork** picks its way through the marshy swamps with eyes

1. **Marabou stork** *(Leptoptilus crumeniferus)*
2. **Saddle-billed stork** *(Ephippiorhynchus senegalensis)*

blinking and alert for eels and lizards. Hearing a frog croaking to his mate, the saddle-bill snakes out its long neck, spies the singer, and in a flash gulps him down, croak and all. Still unsatisfied, it continues hunting until it has added small mammals, small birds and insects to its menu. Then, with a few short jumps, it takes off into the air, keeping its head and neck straight out in front while its stick-like bony legs trail behind. The saddle-billed stork is basically white over the body, but this is broken by black-green on the wings and neck and pink patches on its knobbly knees. Called saddle-billed because of the yellow saddle-like shield on top of its red and black pointed bill, this stork is a mute and makes no sound except by clattering its tremendous bill loudly.

Its other name is the white-bellied stork.

THE UNKNOWN STORK

"Simbil! Simbil" chanted the Sudanese people, kneeling below an **Abdim's stork** in the shade of a grove of mimosa trees. The only answer the worshippers got, was the rather angry clattering of the bill of an odd-looking bird perched in the branches, glaring down at them. Abdim's stork is found in Dongola in the Sudan, but it migrates to South Africa every year. About twenty-five inches tall it is very adept at catching fish, small amphibians and snakes. This bird has one very odd characteristic which makes it completely different from the rest of the stork family: its throat is incomplete and closed with a membrane. It is a very gregarious bird that lives and travels in large groups which dot the East African skies at migration time.

Abdim's stork *(Sphenorynchus abdimii)*

Glossy ibis *(Plegadis falcinellus)*

RELATIVE OF ROYALTY

Four thousand years ago, the Sacred Ibis was one of the most venerated creatures on earth. The ancient Egyptians, believing it to be the incarnation of the god Thoth, built shrines to it, and few Pharaohs would travel or were buried without its exalted company. Reduced, since then, to the rank of ordinary mortal, it has become a very rare bird. A more numerous relative, the **glossy ibis** is found throughout most of the subtropical areas of North America, Eurasia, Africa, and Australia. It lives on a varied diet of crayfish, insects, grasshoppers, slugs, snails and small snakes. During the breeding season, the glossy ibis migrates to temperate climates, and as summers have grown longer and warmer in recent decades, it has lengthened its journeys, reaching even as far north as southern New Jersey in the United States. It is a gregarious bird whose flocks sometimes number thousands, and its large, rippling formations are a familiar sight against the bright spring and autumn skies.

In the Old World the glossy ibis is found in southern Europe, in Africa from the Nile delta to South Africa, in southern and south-east Asia and in Australia. But over this wide area it is only found locally, and it is nothing like as abundant as might be supposed from this seemingly wide distribution. It used to be more common, and one of the reasons, it is believed, for this erratic distribution is its tendency to spread. Often, at the close of the breeding season, both the old birds and the young make erratic flights in all directions, singly or in groups, and they may turn up far beyond the area in which they have bred.

STORK OF THE WHITE NILE

Standing breast deep in the White Nile, a group of grey **whale-headed storks** lower their beaks to the surface of the water. Then with a great flapping of wings, they march about in a semi-circle, and so trap their prey into the shallows. Their giant bill is not only formidable for catching fish, frogs and baby crocodiles, but it can probe into the mud also, and come up with both lungfish and turtles. These storks are found in the southern Sudan, Uganda and eastern Congo, but are not a common sight even there, for they always hunt and breed far from human habitation. The nest is hidden away in the reeds, and may be as high as three feet. Within this construction of stalks, grass, mud and sticks the eggs are laid, very small eggs when compared with the adult bird's forty inches height. If the adult whale-heads are disturbed "at home" by even the far away presence of a boat, they will take flight, snap their beaks in the wind, and soar high into the air until all danger is past.

The whale-headed stork is also known as the bog-bird or the shoebill and even today nobody is sure what are its nearest relatives. Some scientists see it as a kind of heron, others as a kind of stork, and a third view is that it is closer to the pelicans. In this perplexity it has been placed in a separate family of its own. The trouble is caused by its extraordinary bill, which in its shape and the use to which it is put strongly recalls the pelican's bill, whereas in other ways it resembles both herons and storks. The truth is, in all probability, that it springs from the same stock as the herons and storks but has, over a long period of time, taken to special feeding habits and has developed the unusual bill as a consequence.

One feature that links the shoebill with the heron is its powder-down. Herons have patches of powder-down on their chest. A shoebill has its powder-down on its back.

Whale-headed stork (*Balaeniceps rex*)

Sacred ibis (*Threskiornis aethiopica*)

THE BIRD WHO WAS GOD

The Pharoah was dead! His mummified body, with all his treasures and possessions, was placed inside the Pyramid. The last object put in to accompany the Pharoah on his journey was a mummified body of the god Thoth, the recorder of the lives of men who, in his living form, was the **sacred ibis.** Today it is a rare bird, found only in Africa, south of the Sahara. This silvery-white ibis is a beautiful sight when flying in flocks, with its neck straight out in front, its legs stretched out behind, and the slow, strong beat of its wings. It is a study in graceful motion. Its gait on the ground is quiet and deliberate and somewhat misleading to small snakes and lizards. To them the sacred ibis seems to be farther away than it is and they pay little attention to it, but the ibis, moving with extraordinary agility, suddenly has them in its long bill.

THE LONGEST DIVE

Nobody who has ever heard the divers' music, its mournful far-carrying cry, the uninhibited concert of crazy laughter, can ever forget it. It brings back to mind far-away places, the haunting memory of forest lakes where the clear air is scented with balsam and fir, lazy winding rivers, and lonely icy pools in the thawing tundra. If the setting is beautiful so is the bird. The **great northern diver** of North America and Greenland, with its cousin the **black-throated diver** of northern Eurasia and Baffin Island, have slender, sleek, torpedo-shaped bodies, that enable them to dart through the water like arrows after their fish prey. Using their webbed feet to propel themselves, they can chase a despairing victim down to a depth of two hundred and forty feet. On land the diver walks awkwardly because its legs are set far back on the body. So it tumbles and scrambles along, using its feet in the fashion of a seal, pushing itself and scraping its breast on the ground. It has been nicknamed the "Loon" meaning an awkward person. But once it reaches water, a transformation takes place, and our diver is as graceful and acrobatic as a ballet dancer.

Divers, found only in the northern hemisphere, have more prowess in the water than their ability to swim and dive. They are able to submerge slowly, without apparent effort on their part and without a ripple, and when alarmed they can swim with only the head and neck showing above water or even with only the bill showing. This has a particular value in the moulting season. Most birds moult their flight feathers gradually, and as fast as some feathers are lost others grow out to replace them. A bird in moult may look somewhat untidy but it can still fly. A diver moults all its flight feathers simultaneously and for a time, until the new feathers have grown, is flightless. But for their unusual skills in the water they would be very vulnerable then.

Great northern diver (*Gavia immer*)
Black-tnroated diver (*Gavia arctica*)

European coot (*Fulica atra*)

A SILLY BIRD

One of the silliest birds to watch is the **European coot.** Ungainly, ungraceful, it cuts a somewhat ridiculous figure as it flaps its broadly-lobed feet over the water in an effort to build up enough speed to get airborne. Often, rather than fly across a lake or a brackish coastal shoal, it will "skip on water", flapping its wings just enough to keep its body clear of the surface. More proficient in water than in air, the European coot can swim under water for as long as sixteen seconds and dive to a depth of 25 feet after fish and other aquatic animals, although their food is mainly vegetable. Coots are usually seen in large flocks. Considered inedible because of its tough flesh and its "fishy" taste, the coot is thought by hunters

1. **Great crested grebe** (*Podiceps cristatus*)
2. **Horned or Slavonian grebe** (*Podiceps auritus*)

to be a menace because it not only competes with ducks by eating the same food, but also kills ducklings.

THE FLYING SUBMARINE

One or more of the eighteen species of **grebes** are found in practically every part of the world, from Australia to Labrador and from Peru to eastern Asia. They spend even more of their time on the water than their close cousins, the loons. They sleep, eat, court and breed in the water, and are the only birds known to carry their young piggy-back under the water with them when menaced. When danger is near, they can also deflate their bodies and submerge,

Brown pelican (*Pelecanus occidentalis*)

leaving only their heads above water like periscopes. They use their large, lobed feet to propel themselves when chasing fish, crustaceans and frogs which they hunt underwater. Spending their whole lives mainly in fresh water, grebes head north towards their breeding grounds in the summer, stopping for rest and food on freshwater streams and lakes along the way. Should they light on salt water, they keep swimming in the direction of their migration at about 1¼ miles per hour, fishing as they go. The largest is the **great crested grebe.**

White pelican (*Pelecanus onocrotalus*)

THE BROWN BOMB

From a height of thirty feet the big **brown pelican** plunges towards the surface of the sea with half-spread wings, diving straight down. "Boom!" The bird smacks the water with a splash heard half a mile away. No wonder that, so we are told, fish as much as six feet below the surface are stunned. The brown pelican suffers little for under the skin of its breast there are pockets of air that act as shock absorbers. After scooping the fish up into its enormous bill it flies away, draining the water from its down-pointed beak so that it can then swallow its catch. Watch out now for the little gull! Landing on the pelican's head it may steal fish right out of the diver's pouch. The four-foot brown bird does much of its spectacular fishing along the coasts of the United States, from Canada to South America. The pelicans that nest on the islets in the Great Salt Lake, in Utah, which is without fish, have to fly between 30 to 100 miles a day, carrying food for their young from other lakes.

FEATHERED FISH HERDER

At first sight, pelicans look like freaks. The legs seem too weak for their heavy bodies, and the "accordion-like" beaks, when filled to capacity with twelve quarts of water and fish, look extremely top-heavy. Yet, they are superb fliers. Once airborne, hundreds or perhaps thousands of **white pelicans** may pattern the sky in echelon or V-formations, flapping their wings in unison and diving or soaring like well-drilled airmen "mass-flying" at an Air Force review. The secret of their fishing success is teamwork. After they have spotted a school of fish, they land in a semi-circle, with wings held partially open to cast shadows, and begin herding the school towards the shoals. On cue, all in unison, they dip their giant bucket beaks and scoop up the fish in such a successful manoeuvre that the school is almost totally destroyed. During the breeding season, their feet and face turn a bright orange-red and their snowy white plumage is tinted a pretty pastel pink by oil glands secreting this colourful fluid.

The white pelican is found in south-eastern Europe, in southern Asia and in parts of Africa.

1. **Brandt's cormorant** (*Phalacrocorax penicillatus*)
2. **Common cormorant with chick** (*Phalacrocorax carbo*)

**Common
or great cormorant**
(Phalacrocorax carbo)

a nearby coastal cave. Although famous for these salt-water forays, they are not averse to searching rivers and lakes. Indeed, as Brandt's cormorants can dive and fish in even the muddiest streams, there comes the question whether they may not hunt as much with their ears as with their eyes. All this fishing skill is needed when the young are born. The adults build their nests of sticks or guano within a whole colony of perhaps ten thousand other birds. In front of Brandt's cormorant, in this picture, is seen a **common cormorant,** feeding its young.

THE FLEXIBLE TORPEDO

One of the world's slickest swimmers and divers, tunnelling the water like a flexible torpedo, is the **common** or **great cormorant,** one of about thirty different species of cormorants.[*] Its ancestry is reckoned to date back fifty million years. Indeed baby cormorants, which are born blind and naked, look more like prehistoric reptiles than birds, until their feathers grow. They are fed on partly digested fish vomited by their parents and dropped piece by piece into the youngsters' gaping beaks. Later, the ever-greedy chicks cannot wait for this. They thrust their heads far down into their parent's gullet to pluck swallowed fish direct from it. The cormorant never eats its catch under water. It brings its head up and works the fish with its tongue until it can be gulped down head-first. In some Asian countries cormorants are tamed and trained to fish for their owners. A cord around the base of the

American snake bird *(Anhinga anhinga)*

A CITY OF FISHERMEN

Flying low over Mexico's Pacific coast, a flock of **Brandt's cormorants** scan the ocean. When fish are sighted, they land on the water, and then swim low, their bills pointing upwards. Suddenly the raiders lunge over and completely submerge themselves. As their stiff feathers are not really water-proof, they may not stay down too long. So, they either quickly flush the fish up to the surface or drive them into

1. Great frigate bird (*Fregata minor*)

2. White-tailed tropic bird (*Phaethon lepturus*)

neck prevents the bird from swallowing. This is removed from time to time to let the cormorant take its reward for its wonderful skill in the water.

UNDERWATER HARPOON-FISHING

Just before sundown, flocks of **American snake birds** fly up into the air and head straight for their fishing grounds. After landing on the water, they swim about with only their heads and necks exposed, looking just like serpents. But not for long – quickly they submerge, coming up again later far away from where they made their dive. Underwater, their method of fishing is strange and unusual.

When a fish is spied, the snake bird draws its long neck back like a bow. Then it shoots out its sharp bill like an arrow, spearing clean through the victim. The whole action recalls strongly the fashionable sport of harpoonfishing, using an aqua-lung. Then the bird comes to the surface, shakes off its prey with a series of jerks, and swallows it. These raiders live chiefly near freshwater lakes and swamps, from the southern states of America to the Argentine. Waterlands surrounded by woods or filled with little islands are their favourite haunts. In the daytime they sun themselves on a grassy shore. Not far away are their nests, built above the ground in the boughs of trees.

OCEAN MARAUDER

With its wing-span of seven feet, the **great frigate bird** is possessed of a power of flight superior to all other birds. Throughout the Atlantic, Pacific, and Indian Oceans it wheels high, glides steeply and then dives to the very waves to snatch its meals. Fishing, however, is merely a side-line, the bird seeming to prefer raiding its fellows. Many of these "Man-o'-War" birds will follow a flock of gulls or

1. Great black-backed gull (*Larus marinus*)

2. Atlantic puffin (*Fratercula arctica*)

white-tailed tropic birds and wait until they have caught their fish. When this happens, the mid-air tussle will begin. The swift gannet, known as a booby, does not give up its meal as easily as the others, so the great frigate bird slashes at its tail with its long bill. The booby is still unco-operative, but when seized by the

tail, it receives a shake it never forgets. Sooner or later any bird chased in this way by a frigate bird will drop its catch. The robber then dives and overtakes the falling fish before it hits the sea.

BLACK-BACKED ASSASSIN

A sinister black shadow sweeps across a puffin flying home with food for her young. Before she can escape, the shadow takes form. With a powerful beating of its five-foot wings and vicious pecking of its hooked bill, the **black-backed gull** strikes the poor puffin to earth and devours her. Although the word "gull" is a synonym in many languages for "fool", the black-backed predator can be rather clever when it comes to robbing others for food. As a duck surfaces with its bill crammed with fish, the black-backed pirate will perch on its back, and whilst maintaining its balance with its wings, will snatch the catch literally from under the duck's nose. Two black-backs will often work together, one keeping a mother guillemot distracted while the other steals the egg. Cowardly and vicious to the young and helpless, the black-backed gull will attack and kill wounded ducks or snatch out the eyes of new-born lambs. Unhappily, the mother ewe, who is formidable and courageous when fighting foxes, seems absolutely powerless when it comes to staving off an attack from the skies.

RAIDERS OF THE SEVEN SEAS

On the facing page are some of the wonderful sea-birds seen in various seas today. Their ancestors must have lived in exactly the same way when the mutineers of the "Bounty" were sailing for Pitcairn Island. First comes the **magnificent frigate,** or "Man-o'-War" bird, whose huge red pouch develops only during courtship. Of all sea-birds this is by far the fastest flier. Air speeds of over 100 miles an hour have been recorded. Its body is so perfectly constructed as a flying machine that it can ride a hurricane which whirls away all other birds as if they were paper. The magnificent frigate uses its incredible speed to overtake other birds and force them to drop their catches, then it darts down and snatches the fish in mid-air. Why it has to rob in this way is because it cannot itself swim or dive for its food, for the weakness of its legs would prevent a "take-off" from the water. So, although it can fly fast and far, it can only land on cliffs, rocks or tall trees. Next, top of the picture, is the

1. **Magnificent frigate** (*Fregate magnificens*)
2. **Fulmar** (*Fulmarus glacialis*)
3. **Wandering albatross** (*Diomedia exulans*)
4. **Storm petrel** (*Hydrobates pelagicus*)
5. **Yellow-billed tropic bird** (*Phaethon lepturus*)
6. **Arctic tern** (*Sterna paradisaea*)
7. **Black-headed gull**(*Larus ridibundus*)
8. **Great skua** (*Catharacta skua*)
9. **Manx shearwater** (*Puffinus puffinus*)
10. **Ring-billed gull** (*Larus delawarensis*)
11. **Red-footed booby** (*Sula sula*)
12. **Herring gull** (*Larus argentatus*)
13. **Razorbill or razor-billed auk** (*Alca torda*)

fulmar, actually an arctic bird, but migrating as far south as Japan. If attacked it has a better defence than judo, as it can spit an evil-smelling fluid to a distance of a yard or more. Biggest of all these sea-raiders is the **wandering albatross** with a record wing-span of eleven and a half feet. It is a master of soaring flight, whose structure and performance in the air both designers and pilots of sailplanes have been able to copy. Yet, no man-made glider could hope

51

to compete with the wandering albatross who has been known to follow a ship for three thousand miles. With a following wind he can attain speeds of over one hundred miles an hour. Next on the right is the smallest web-footed bird, the **storm petrel** or "Mother Cary's Chicken". The nickname is very old, deriving from the exclamation "Mater Cara" (Dear Mother), an appeal to the Virgin Mary, when petrels were seen heralding a storm. It can stay at sea for weeks on end, feeding mostly on plankton, the tiny specks of marine food which make the ocean larder for countless millions of its inhabitants. But it is also a raider preying on little fish, and it often follows steamers to pick up crustaceans and cuttle-fish churned up by the screw. Immediately below the albatross is the **yellow-billed tropic bird** with its distinctive elongated tail. At the base of the tail is a gland secreting oil with which it makes its plumage waterproof! Next to it is the **Arctic tern,** the amazing "daylight raider" who breeds during the arctic summer and migrates to the antarctic summer before the dark northern winter sets in. The little bird on the left is the **black-headed gull;** then comes the savage **great skua** which lives by robbery and murder. It steals eggs and other birds' catches of fish, killing their young and even fully-grown birds with an extraordinary ferocity. The one with the fish in its beak is the **shearwater,** long-distance champion of homing flights, and below the "Bounty's" ensign is the **ring-billed gull,** one of the forty-three species distributed over the world. In front of it, about to splash feet first into the water, is the **red-footed booby,** tropical counterpart of the gannet. It is called booby because it is easy to catch, but it is no booby at catching fish. It comes down with such a smack that fish are stunned by the impact, and made easy prey. Next on the left is the **herring gull,** often seen flying inland. It cracks the hard shells of molluscs or crabs by dropping them onto sea walls or pavements. But it has not learnt to recognise its own chicks if they stray from the nest, for it will kill and eat them as greedily as it will the young of other birds. Last in the picture is the **razor-billed auk,** a smoothly plumaged bird about sixteen inches long. It is a marvellous diver, and will plunge down to the sea-bed to pick up its prey. Truly each of these birds is a wonderful example of adaptation to the business of living by raiding, in one form or another. For them there is no other way.

Sea lamprey (*Petromyzon marinus*)

VAMPIRE OF THE LAKES

In less than a generation the **lamprey** destroyed an entire industry – the commercial fishing on the Great Lakes of North America. Originally a sea-dweller, the lampreys became accomodated to life in fresh water where enemies are fewer and food is plentiful. Unable to ascend the torrential rapids of the St. Lawrence River, they had to make a detour around them, working their way up nearby canals until they reached the teeming lakes. Thirty years after this happened an annual catch of eleven million pounds of trout and other fish had been reduced to nearly zero, the once bulging fishing boats were gone, and hundreds of fisherman had to look elsewhere for work. The lamprey is an active parasite that attaches itself to fish with its large round sucker-like mouth which is lined with some 115 sharp teeth. These teeth rasp and scrape the thin skin of the fish until it starts to bleed. The lamprey then hangs on while sucking out its host's life-blood. When its victim is drained nearly to death, this lethal parasite swims swiftly over to the next, and the next and the next.

HUNGRY HORROR OF THE SURF

The **great white shark** is "the" man-eater of the shark family. Though not numerous, this brute kills more swimmers each year than any other type of shark. It frequents shallows where the sea-bed drops off sharply from the shoreline, such as along the Pacific coast of America, and the coasts of Australia and South Africa. The great white shark has claimed kills in as little as four feet of water and often ventures into the first line of breakers. A massive beast it may grow to over 36 feet and weigh thousands of pounds. It will eat anything and has been known to attack rowing boats. In Hawaii, these ravenous man-eaters have pulled people from rafts and surfboards barely yards from shore, dragging them down to deaths of horror in the glistening surf, dismembering them bite by bite, striking, wheeling, striking, and turning to strike again. In 1799, when Britain was at war with the Netherlands, the American brig "Nancy" was intercepted in the West Indies by HMS "Sparrow" and charged with trading in contraband arms.

Great white shark (*Carcharodon carcharias*)

Ship and captain would have gone free for lack of evidence save that the papers proving the captain's guilt, which he had thrown overboard, were found in the stomach of a captured white shark just in the nick of time. Although called "white", the colour of this shark may be slate-grey, blue, brown or almost black.

STREAMLINED MURDERER

A large fish swam quickly along through its watery home. A **mako shark** spotted it and gave chase overtaking the speeding fugitive with every sweep of its flashing tail. The mako caught the fish in seconds, and with one snap of its vicious jaws bit off the victim's tail, thus leaving the head and half the body to drift helplessly whilst waiting for the executioner's coup de grace. A champion swimmer, the mako's over thirty knot speed quickly dooms its slower prey. Small fish it gulps whole, sparing them the pain of its sharp teeth. Found in most of the warmer seas of the world, this streamlined scourge often grows to over nine feet in length and can weigh over half a ton. It is the favourite shark of deep-sea anglers because, when hooked, it puts up a tremendous fight, sometimes leaping as much as thirty feet out of the water. Though not a deliberate man-eater, like the white shark, it is unreliable and should be given a wide berth.

Mako shark (*Isurus oxyrhynchus*)

SHY EYES

Sharks are spread widely throughout the warm seas, and belong to many distinct species. One of these is the **catshark,** found in the inshore waters of South Africa, and called by the old Dutch name of "Skaamog", or "Shy Eye". The name came from its extraordinary habit, when disturbed, of curling its tail right over its head, thus hiding its eyes. Some say it does this because it thinks that if it cannot see an enemy, that enemy cannot see it – as an ostrich is alleged to put its head in the sand. But it probably has a better reason – perhaps to show off its very strange body markings. These are amazingly like old Egyptian hieroglyphics arranged in coloured patterns, and are quite unique. The catshark preys on other fish, and grows to a length of about three feet. Its eggs are rectangular, with a single tendril at each corner.

GREAT BLUE SHARK

Although it is known and almost welcomed as an eater of surplus fish, rotting flesh and the garbage of many ocean waters, there is something coldly horrible about the way the **great blue shark** destroys its larger victims. Maybe a man fallen overboard, a wounded porpoise, or a dead or dying member of its own kind. It makes no difference. The shark starts to swim slowly around its intended prey, then more quickly, getting closer at each turn. Suddenly it darts in, jaws agape, and draws the first blood. From that instant it goes berserk, eating its way along the body with madly gnashing teeth. Often many sharks join in the feast. If one should be accidentally injured so

Catshark (*Holobalaelurus regani*)

that blood flows, it is instantly torn to pieces by the others. The great blue shark grows to about 12 feet long, but is slender-bodied, therefore light for its size. It makes up in ferocity what it lacks in bulk.

Great blue shark (*Prianace glauca*)

55

Dr. JEKYLL AND Mr. HYDE

Off the coast of Florida an experienced skin-diver will ignore a **sand shark** that circles curiously around him. He knows that this prowler has no record of having deliberately attacked human beings. On the same day, half way round the world, a bather may be viciously attacked by exactly the same kind of fish, and badly mauled before he can struggle to the safety of the beach. A docile "Dr. Jekyll" in one ocean, the sand shark can be a raging "Mr. Hyde" in the shallow waters of another, as on the coast of East Africa. Very rarely does it rest on the sea-bed, as others do, for it seems to have a compelling urge to be constantly on the move, either in search of prey, or for the purpose of rushing to attack everything that moves on or under the surface. It is, in fact, completely unreliable. It has been known, after taking no notice of hippos enjoying a dip in the wide estuaries of south-east Africa and living at peace with them for weeks, to suddenly turn on even these most formidable

intruders, and to slash through their tough hides with its rows of dagger-like teeth. Even before leaving its parent's body the killer instinct is with the sand shark for it is said that as soon as it has digested the egg-yolk with which it is nourished before birth, it will turn cannibal, and attack its unhatched relations.

HIDDEN DEMON OF THE PEACEFUL LAKE

High in the jungles of Central America, Lake Nicaragua lies shimmering amid green hills in a setting of breath-taking beauty, inviting the passer-by to escape the oppressive heat in the coolness of its waters. But this can

Sand shark *(Carcharias taurus)*

be an invitation to death, for under its calm surface lurks one of the world's few fresh water maneaters, the **Lake Nicaragua shark.** Averaging 8 to 10 feet in length and closely related to the Atlantic ground shark which rarely attacks men, this predator was originally a sea-dweller who migrated up the San Carlos River from the Caribbean. When prehistoric earthquakes cut off its return route to the sea with waterfalls and rapids, this shark settled down in its present home and somehow acquired a taste for people. The Lake Nicaragua

shark is a deadly menace to swimmers in the lakeshore shallows because it hugs the bottom, so that no racing fin breaks the surface to warn of its approach. Local people and visitors alike have succumbed to its stealth, their first hint of danger being the mortal crush of the murderer's powerful jaws.

WHITE HAMMER OF DEATH

The **hammerhead shark** is fearsome to behold. Its broad flat head, sometimes measuring three feet across, flanked by two evil black eyes that peer out from the ends, makes it look like a living hammer. Its long body reflects the filtered sunlight of the depths as it glides slowly along or suddenly flashes after some attractive morsel. Its eternally grumpy expression matches its disposition, and its mouth opens to reveal a set of cruel teeth that are the terror of nearly every animal that moves on or under the sea. Sometimes growing up to fifteen feet long and weighing three-quarters of a ton, the hammerhead has killed or maimed many bathers along the world's beaches. Primarily a fish-eater which frequents tropical waters, this surly killer is fearless, and will

Hammerhead shark *(Sphyrna zygaena)*

Lake Nicaragua shark

(Carcharinus nicaraguensis)

attack anything it sees moving in the water. Woe be to the swimmer or skin-diver it spots with its wide-set eyes, for nothing short of killing it will stop the hammerhead's relentless attack.

THE SHARK TURNED DETECTIVE

In 1935 a **tiger shark** once solved a murder mystery. A few days after it was captured and brought to an aquarium in Sydney, Australia, the shark coughed up the tattooed arm of a man. A piece of rope was tied to the wrist. Using the tattoo mark as a clue police were able to trace the arm to a man who had recently disappeared, and ultimately convicted the murderers who had disposed of his dismembered body in the sea. Thus, one heartless killer helped to bring some of his human counterparts to justice. The tiger shark is well known for being a glutton. Anything that swims, crawls, floats, or lies on the bottom, or even a bird that lights on the surface, is fair game for its fancy. Often reaching eighteen feet and weighing over 1500 pounds, it gets its name from the tiger-like stripes that decorate its powerful back. Its ferocity is notorious. It will chase fish into shallow water until it

Tiger shark *(Galeocerdo cuvieri)*

nearly strands itself, but if it finds that its agile prey has eluded it, it can just as readily turn man-eater as its namesake on land.

We usually think of sharks turning on their backs to snap at a victim swimming at the surface. This has been perpetuated in adventure stories and in the imaginative drawings made to illustrate them. A shark will turn on its back in this way, but only to gobble offal, carrion or other refuse floating at the surface. It does this lazily, as for example when garbage is thrown overboard and people have time to watch it equally leisurely.

The tiger shark exploits this. It has the trick of inflating its body and wallowing in the water in a fair representation of a floating carcass. Other sharks drawing near to inspect this seeming piece of carrion turn over lazily to snap at it thus exposing the soft underbelly to attack by the tiger shark.

One good thing can be said of sharks: that they supply numerous products. Their flesh is eaten in some parts of the world and their skin makes a durable leather for shoes and handbags.

THIS BANDIT HUNTS IN PACKS!

A dweller in Mediterranean and eastern Atlantic waters, the **deep-sea spiny dogfish** seldom exceeds two feet in length, but it is a terror to all forms of life in the neighbourhood, for it is a wholesale killer. Often it seems to kill for the sake of killing, and it is a voracious feeder. In addition to the spines which give it its name, it has large eyes, and on its sides are luminous organs which help either

to attract inquisitive victims or to perceive them in the gloomy ocean depths. Travelling in swiftly moving shoals, it carries out mass raids on other fish, in pursuit of which it will often come up into the upper levels of the sea to cause great damage to fishing gear and nets. If it is caught there is no profit to be made since there is no demand in the markets either for its flesh or its skin. It is lucky for other fish that its rate of reproduction is low, the number of eggs hatched each summer being from 20 to 25 only.

ARCTIC KILLERS

A group of seals are gathered on an ice shelf.

Deep-sea spiny dogfish *(Etmopterus spinax)*

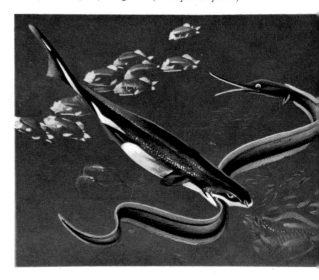

basking in the brilliant sunlight of the Arctic summer. Nearby, others frisk in the chilly waters. Suddenly, a warning bark sends the swimmers scattering in mortal flight as a huge shape surfaces, weaving savagely through their disordered ranks. By the time the last survivor has clambered back onto the safety of the shelf, several of their number have disappeared forever beneath the blood-stained waves, victims of the giant **Greenland shark.** In Lapland, herds of reindeer on migration swim between the islands, and some never reach the shore. Largest of the species of dogfish that live in the cold oceans near the poles, this massive monster often exceeds 20 feet in length and frequently weighs over a ton. Fishermen seek it out for the valuable oil found in its liver – over 30 gallons in a really big one. Though this ferocious predator can swallow a seal or reindeer whole, when caught by man it gives itself up with the meekness of a lamb.

It is easy enough to draw attention to the ferocity of a shark, and to do so is to provide the kind of spectacular reading that most of us enjoy, secretly or openly. The other side of the picture is that which the Greenland shark illustrates well, the role of scavenger played by sharks in general. While this particular species feeds mainly on seals and fish, sometimes on crabs, it also takes a great deal of offal and carrion. Possibly, if the truth were known it takes more of this than of live prey, if we may judge by its nickname, "the sleeper". This seems to have been bestowed on it because of its slow and sluggish way of swimming.

Perhaps, as is the case in some other species, the leopard seal being a good example, an animal gets a bad name from what it is some-times seen doing. The leopard seal will eat penguins when it is near a penguin rookery, and this is what it is most often seen doing. When, however, a scientific study was made of the leopard seal it was found that it ate fish and squid habitually and only ate penguins occasionally. So with the Greenland shark. When it is seen attacking seals that is enough to give it a bad name. The fact that it is by nature a relatively lethargic swimmer suggests that it is more given to taking food that cannot move out of its way quickly. Certain it is that a dead whale will attract large numbers of Greenland sharks; and these same sharks are numerous off the coast of Alaska where they feed on the refuse from the salmon canneries.

Greenland shark *(Somniosus microcephalus)*

61

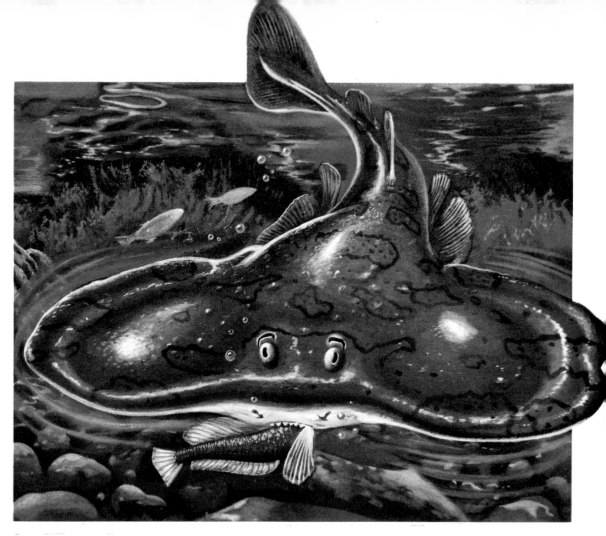

Electric ray (*Torpedo* sp.)

SHOCKING MURDER

Effectively blocking all means of escape, the **electric ray** neatly folds its pancake-like body around its struggling victim, turns on the current, and shocks the fish to death. The power plant of this extraordinary fish is located in the broadened fins near its head. Some members of this electric family can produce 220 volts – that of an ordinary house current and more than enough to knock a man out. When put into an aquarium with some leopard sharks, a frightened ray sent out such violent shock waves that these large fish leaped into the air in giant spasms of terror and pain. Hampered by poor eyesight, the electric ray transmits micro-voltage waves similar to an under-water radar and these guide it around obstacles and enable it to communicate with its high-powered friends. This live wire would probably electrocute more fish than are its right, except that periodically it runs out of power and needs several days for recharging.

AS BROAD AS HE IS LONG

One of the strangest and most fearsome-looking objects inhabiting the warmer seas is the giant **eagle ray,** averaging fourteen to

Eagle ray (*Myliobatis nieuhofi*)

fifteen feet in length and width. Its speed through the water is quite remarkable because of the way it uses its "wings", with a kind of waving motion, more like a bird in flight. Its long whip-like tail helps mainly in steering, but is also used for defence. A slash from this viciously curling weapon could cut a pursuing enemy in half. But the eagle ray is always the hunter rather than the hunted, its prey being almost exclusively shellfish, including crabs, lobsters and especially oysters and clams. These it can grind almost to powder between the pavement-like teeth which form surfaces in both upper and lower jaws. It is doubtful whether even this giant can do much with the giant clam seen in this picture. The young rays are born alive, with their wings folded round their bodies, so that from the first they look as strange as their parents.

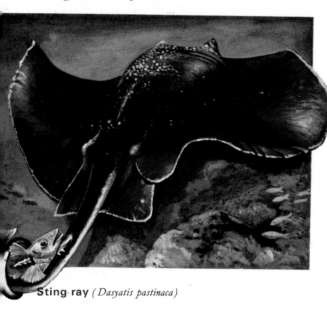

Sting ray (*Dasyatis pastinaca*)

THE STING OF DEATH

With what looks like murder gleaming in its small evil eyes, the **sting ray** lies waiting to seize any small or medium-sized fish that may swim within striking range. Should anything large prove to be a menace, it will lash out with its whip-like tail. The actual lethal part of this weapon is a spine which protrudes half-way down the tail and is notched along both edges with a row of sharp tiny barbs. The structure of this spine is like that of a tooth, with dentine and enamel and a pulp cavity. In a groove running along either side of the spine is a tissue secreting venom. A swimmer who is

slashed by this is likely to suffer considerable pain, and he may die either of shock or of a heart-failure. This sting ray is found in warm temperate waters from the Atlantic to the Pacific and unfortunately prefers the shallows often used by bathers. In the United States alone, this submerged viper, camouflaged by its brownish skin, wounds each year over 1,500 waders who accidentally step on it.

A PANCAKE FISH

Looking like a much flattened ray, about as broad as it is long, the **American skate** is a familiar sight on the quays of fishing ports, and on fishmongers' slabs in North American towns. But it has points of interest far greater than its value as a sea-food. One peculiarity is its method of feeding. Since its eyes are on top of its flattened head and its mouth underneath, the skate must glide slowly just above the sea-bed, searching for food by smell or touch. When it locates a crab or a fish, it flops suddenly down on it, smothering it under its body and then working it along until the prey can be taken into its mouth. The female lays flat four-cornered eggs, each one in a case of keratin, which is a substance similar to that of our fingernails. Each corner of the egg-case has a sort of hook which helps to anchor it to seaweeds, false-corals or any support of this kind under the water.

American skate (*Raja eglanteria*)

Sawfish *(Pristis pectinatus)*

SAWFISH

School is finished for the day when the monster **sawfish** begins flailing its deadly weapon from side to side and causing a riot in the peaceful waters of the West Indies. Schools of darting fish streak for their lives; but some are too late and are wounded by or impaled on the sharp merciless spikes of the sawfish's double-edged saw. With mighty strokes of its tail it rounds up the few strays before leisurely dining on its stunned or injured victims. Its hors d'oeuvres is found by using this same handy instrument to dig for crustaceans hiding in the sand. Although this mammoth can grow to a length of 35 feet and can weigh up to 5,000 pounds, divers rarely fear it for it will never intentionally attack humans. In fact, to catch the sawfish, divers swim behind it, grab its fins and guide it into the shallow waters where it can be dragged by means of ropes onto the shore. Yet sawfish are dreaded in parts of India, where it is declared one of them once cut a bather in two with a sweep of its saw.

EASY FEEDER

In the big eastern and southern rivers of the U.S.A. dead or injured fish are common enough, and it is on this easy prey that the **longnose gar** chiefly feeds. Head pointed upstream, it can "hover" patiently, knowing that the current will bring it all it needs. Though sometimes carried by the force of the current to salty estuaries, it is essentially a freshwater fish. Its average length is about four feet, the nose contributing more to it than in the case of any other gar. The jaws have long, very sharp teeth, with which the longnose gar grabs its food with a kind of sideways slash. In the south spawning takes place in March or April, later in the colder waters of the north. Because the eggs are adhesive, and therefore stick to river-bed vegetation in weedy shallows,

Longnose gar *(Lepisosteus osseus)*

nests are not made, nor is there any guarding of the eggs during incubation. The adult fish is protected by thick scales, tough enough to turn aside a skin-diver's spear.

HARD-WORKING PAPA

It is curious to think of any fish as the hard-working father of a family, but the **bowfin** is more than that. He "fathers" many families at once. He builds a round nest to receive the eggs of several females, and then fertilises the eggs in numbers of up to 30,000 or more. He then faithfully guards them for a week or so until they hatch. After this he continues to keep a fatherly eye on them till Nature takes over. She has provided newly-hatched bowfins with an adhesive snout, so they can cling to water plants until able to swim after food. They

Bowfin *(Amia calva)*

also have a swim-bladder which acts as a lung enabling the bowfins to take in air at the surface, and survive in water with a low oxygen content, or even stay alive without water for as long as 24 hours. Incredibly voracious eaters, they consume huge numbers of amphibians, crustaceans, worms and small fry, even larger fishes though always hunting alone. In some parts of the United States bowfin are so numerous and so destructive that measures have to be taken against them. In cold winters their vital processes slow down, as in the case of hibernating animals.

Tarpon (*Megalops atlanticus*)

SEA-GOING DYNAMITE

A fast swimmer, the **tarpon** is a favourite of the American sport fishermen because of its explosive reaction to the hook. Making a swift rush to the surface, it leaps high into the air in an effort to shake loose the steel barb lodged in its throat. The ensuing battle between fighting fish and exultant fisherman, punctuated by the tarpon's ten foot leaps out of the water, ends only when the fish is totally exhausted. Living in tropical and sub-tropical waters, it migrates to shallower regions to spawn. Living on a diet of fish, it ranges out into deep water to hunt, well equipped for the chase by virtue of its speed and the many small, sharp teeth set in its narrow jaws. The record tarpon taken on the line was eight feet long and weighed 340 pounds.

The tarpon, which also occurs off the West Indies and off the tropical west coast of Africa, as well as off the entire tropical and sub-tropical east coasts of America, has attracted much attention as something of a mystery fish as well as being a sporting fish. The full-grown fish has a tall back fin, large silvery scales, a jutting lower jaw and large eyes, and it is capable of making tremendous leaps from the water, especially when it has been hooked. In contrast to the showy and conspicuous adult the young tarpon have managed to efface themselves and this led to a considerable mystery about the breeding habits of the tarpon. For a long time it was believed that tarpon make extensive migrations to breed. This has now proved to be incorrect, largely as the result of tagging, a method which, like bird-ringing enables us to trace the movements of particular individuals. It is now thought that very young tarpon spend their time in almost landlocked pools around the coasts, in muddy sulphurous waters lacking oxygen. The grown tarpon has a lung-like air bladder and can take in air as it rolls at the surface. Probably the young fish do the same, and living in stagnant waters helps them escape enemies.

The great leaps, like those of the salmon, are accomplished by the fish swimming rapidly upwards through the surface and giving a sharp flick with its tail as it leaves the water. While wholly immersed in water the muscles of the whole body are brought into play to drive the fish. As soon as it enters the air, which is much less dense than water, its speed increases considerably and that last flick of the tail is enough to drive it well upwards into the air.

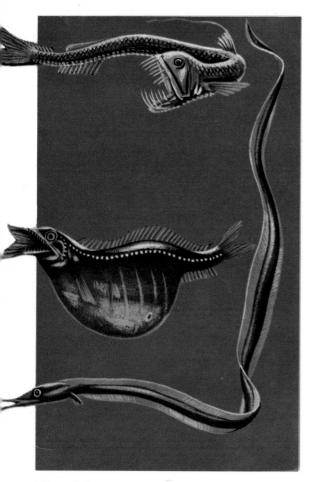

In doing so it throws its head back, lifts its upper jaw and drops the lower jaw. The bones of the spine just behind the head are so constructed that the spine is very supple, making this wide gape possible.

This elaborate mechanism is necessary because the viper fish living in the deep seas where food is not abundant must take advantage of every meal that comes its way.

THE GLUTTON OF THE DEEP

In the cold still depths of the Atlantic Ocean lurks the **black swallower,** its long body with its smooth scaleless skin and its slender teeth, as well as its blackish colouring, giving it a most sinister appearance. This is in keeping with its environment, for its world is one of perpetual gloom, a region where few, if any rays of light ever penetrate. These depths, between nine hundred and four thousand five hundred feet, are the natural habitat of this little fish. Its small size, it is only nine inches long, belies its enormous appetite. It has an extraordinary capacity for devouring, in one piece, other fish much bigger than itself. Scientists are still in some doubt about the way it manages to perform such a feat. One thing is certain, the black swallower cannot be said to have eyes bigger than its stomach.

RIBBON OF LIFE

Far below the sunlit surface of the Mediterranean and other warm seas – at recorded depths of 3,000 to 6,000 feet – swims the **snipe eel,** weaving gently through the water like a translucent ribbon. Dormant by day, it forages at night, its upper and lower jaws curving away from each other forming a slender scoop, its prominent eyes fixed on perpetual darkness in the cold and gloomy depths of its undersea world. It is so slight and slender, and is so much a part of the sea that it is nearly invisible even in the powerful light of submarine lamps. Seldom more than three feet long, the big question is about the way it feeds. It seems that the jaws are permanently wide apart, and it has been suggested that it feeds much as a swallow does in the air, by sweeping any small animals into its mouth as it swims along. The comparison is not very apt because a swallow can close its beak. All we know for certain about the diet of the snipe eel is that deep-sea prawns, two inches long, have been found in the stomachs of snipe eels.

Viper fish *(Chauliodus sloani)*
Black swallower *(Chiasmodus niger)*
Snipe eel *(Nemichthys scolopaceus)*

BURIAL AT SEA

The **viper fish** lives in the depths of tropical oceans. The exact depths needs some explanation. In the Atlantic Ocean, where there are several related species living more or less together, and are competing for food, this species stays at greater depths throughout, between 3,000 and 5,000 feet. In the Malayan Archipelago, where it is on its own, it migrates upwards towards the surface at sunset, spending the day at depths between 1,500 and 9,000 feet. Another peculiarity is that the roof of the mouth is lighted by over 300 small light-organs. Since it must suck water into its mouth to breathe, the water then passing over the gills, small animals attracted to the lights in the open mouth are sucked in and swallowed. However, the sea viper, with the tips of its teeth barbed, can swallow much larger prey.

Snake fish or lizard-fish *(Trachinocephalus myops)*

THE SHARP TEETH OF DEATH

Although this is a fish, it looks and acts like a reptile that is half-snake and half-lizard – hence its common names. It lives in shallow coastal waters of the Atlantic between South Carolina in the north and Brazil in the south, and it lies for hours on sandy, rock-strewn beds waiting for something to eat. As soon as a small fish comes near enough, the **snakefish** darts up like an uncoiling spring, and usually swallows its prey at one gulp, in one flashing movement. Even if the fish is able to dodge and avoid this instantaneous fate, it cannot hope to escape once the stiletto-sharp teeth of the snakefish have gained a hold. Where a sandy sea-bed is soft enough the snakefish sometimes burrows down with the aid of its pectoral fins till only its eyes are visible. But it can still shoot up in an instant, shrugging off the sand with one wriggle of its lithe body. The white larval form of the snakefish does not even vaguely resemble the adult until it has grown to a length of two inches or more.

The snakefish is also found in the Pacific.

THE DELICATE KILLER

Woe betide any fish that gets within striking distance of the **lancet fish's** razor-sharp fang-like teeth. Its six foot long, thin, silver body with its high dorsal fin, extending from behind its head almost to its tail, would be a dreaded sight among the denizens of the ocean, except that it lives at depths where there is little light. As it roams its hunting grounds, the middle depths of the Pacific Ocean, it devours any living thing that crosses its path. Although it is such a savage killer, its body is so delicate that

Pacific lancet fish *(Alepisaurus borealis)*

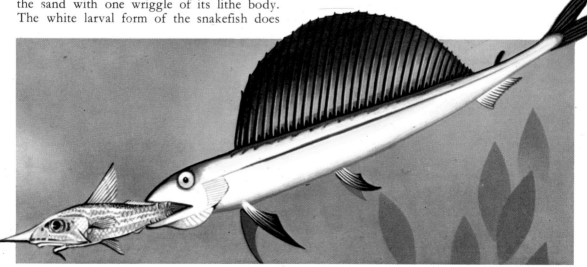

68

Red piranha *(Serrasalmus rhombeus)*

even a light blow is enough to wound it and this makes it very difficult to bring the lancet fish to the surface in a deep-sea fishing net without damaging it. Occasionally its prey has a belated revenge, when the lancet fish may be forced to the surface by swallowing food that increases the buoyancy of its body. Incidentally, it is a great help to students of marine life, because inside the stomachs of captured lancet fish are sometimes discovered rare types of deep-sea fishes.

Piranha or caribe *(Serrasalmus piraya)*

BLOODY BUTCHER OF THE RIVERS

The most ferocious of all living creatures exists not on land, but in the fresh waters of South American rivers. It is the much-dreaded **piranha** or **caribe,** that is irresistibly attracted to blood. No animal, however big, or even a man attempting to ford a piranha-infested stream, can hope to survive if their skin is even slightly scratched. The piranha will instantly attack, and scores, even hundreds of its kind, will rush to the kill, literally slicing their victim to shreds in a matter of minutes. An authentic instance occurred in eastern Brazil, where a horse including its saddle was destroyed in five minutes. This butchery is easy for the killer because its teeth are serrated and sharp enough to cut through flesh and sinew at one snap. Even if a victim drags himself ashore, the piranha still clings, viciously biting to the last moment of its life. Anglers fishing for piranha, for the sake of its delicate flesh, have to use a specially strong hook and line. Ordinary tackle would be snapped like cotton.

THE MADNESS OF CROWDS

One morning, deep in the Amazon jungle, a native woman cut her hand while washing

clothes on the flat stones set in the bank of the small stream bordering her village. Forgetful, she waded into the dark water to wash away the blood. Suddenly, the stream came alive, churning with **piranhas** in a hungry frenzy. Hearing her screams, the villagers rushed to her rescue, but in the brief moment it took to reach her, these ferocious fish had reduced her body to shreds. Hundreds such stories are told of the fanatical fury of these fish, but oddly, the piranha in captivity undergoes a strange transformation, and becomes almost a different fish. Alone or with only one or two others, it becomes nervous and jittery, easily frightened by a sudden movement outside the aquarium tank. Still capable of slicing a piece off another fish in the tank, the lonely piranha seldom demonstrates the boldness it possesses when surrounded by others of its kind.

BEWARE OF POISON

Death lurks in the waters around the tropical reefs of the Indo-Pacific oceans; death from the poisonous spines of the **marine catfish.** Of small size, averaging no more than ten to twelve inches in length, this predator carries its poison in one dorsal and two pectoral spines, each spine with its own poison glands, operating automatically at the least pressure. If a diver or swimmer or a man overboard happened to fall in with a school of marine catfish he might well pay the penalty with his life, merely through accidental contact with the skin-piercing spines. The marine catfish does not deliberately attack anything other than the little fish or small crustaceans it lives on.

Marine catfish (*Plotosus anguillaris*)

However, in the sandy or muddy shallows in Pacific coastal waters, or wherever there is a chance of encountering this carrier of automatic poison, it is best to give it a wide berth. This is not always easy since the catfish sometimes enter estuaries and rivers in large numbers.

Electric catfish (*Malapterurus electricus*)

70

SHOCKING THIEF

Like a bandit with a finger always on the trigger of a gun, the **electric catfish** is the most rapacious of freshwater fish. It lords it among muddy streams and shallows of tropical central Africa and the Nile valley, where its weapon is an electric shock. With a hundred-volt discharge it paralyses its victims and then devours them with ferocious gluttony. A smaller shock is enough to make another fish disgorge its prey, as in the picture, which also shows clearly the six whisker-like barbels round the mouth of the catfish. Apart from fish the greedy thug also snatches at any amphibian or small animal luckless enough to invade its territory. Since it may grow up to four feet long, and fifty pounds in weight, the electric catfish would be a formidable enemy even without its "batteries". If captured and kept in an aquarium tank containing surplus food, it would quickly kill itself with over-eating.

BIRD-EATING MONSTER

This dramatic picture shows a European catfish, the **wels,** in the act of taking a small fish. In its rush it has churned up the mud in which it has lain in ambush at the bottom of a lake. A monster sometimes growing to twelve feet in length, it is the terror of many European lakes and rivers east of the Rhine. For it is not only fishes, frogs and crustaceans that disappear into its capacious mouth. It often plucks down by the feet, ducks and other water-birds swimming on the surface. Of its barbels – the trailing feelers which are rather fancifully compared to a cat's whiskers – the upper pair are a great deal longer than the head, and may be anything from six to ten feet long, according to the age and size of the fish. Head and body are naked; that is they have no scales. Eggs are laid at mid-summer, carelessly in shallow places. Only a tiny percentage survive to become the monsters of the deeper waters.

Wels *(Silurus glanis)*

RIPPER OF THE REEFS

A curious fish nuzzled the hole in the reef, looking for a tidbit. Suddenly, a face as ugly as death itself shot out of the hole. In an instant, fish and face were gone. Back inside again, the **moray eel** waited eagerly for its next meal to come by. One of several species that haunt the offshore reefs of temperate and tropic seas, this fearsome demon keeps to its "cave" by day, venturing out only at night to forage for molluscs, sea-urchins, and other sea-bed dwellers. Measuring 4 to 10 feet, some morays are considered delicacies; however, others are lethally poisonous when eaten. The moray has a vicious disposition, and when it bites, it twists violently, ripping away jagged chunks of flesh with its razor-sharp teeth, and doing

Moray eel (*Muraena helena*)

Dragon moray eel (*Muraena pardalis*)

horrible damage to muscles and tendons. According to sober estimates morays seldom attack human beings without provocation. Where injury is sustained it is usually due to somebody pushing his foot or hand into a crevice where the moray is hiding.

DIRTY WRIGGLER

A sinewy snakelike killer, that lurks in ambush among coral reefs, sunken ships, caves and crevices, in Hawaiian waters, is the fearsome **dragon moray eel,** whose average length is four to five feet, although some specimens have been reported as reaching twice that size. Divers often see it undulating sinuously along the sea-bed looking for prey. Its jaws are immensely powerful, and armed with needle-sharp incurving teeth adapted for grasping and tearing. For this reason its bite is particularly crushing and destructive. Such deadly equipment is more than adequate for feeding purposes, as the Hawaiian dragon lives mostly on small fish and invertebrates that can be easily bitten through and swallowed in an instant. Therefore the armament of the dragon moray must be defensive. Its teeth are not known to be poisonous, but as its habits are dirty, since it is not above eating carrion, a bite may well cause infection. Fortunately the fish is not aggressive when men visit its haunts, but quickly retires to its lair.

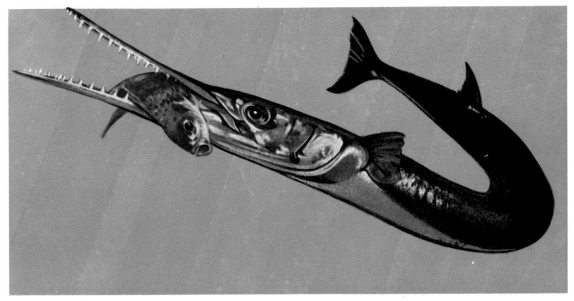

Atlantic needlefish *(Strongylura marina)*

A FLYING MURDERER

Strong, long-jawed, ferocious, this inhabitant of central Atlantic waters has often been mistaken for a flying fish. This is because the **Atlantic needlefish** feeds on the surface of the sea, and when pursued or excited, becomes violently agitated and will make enormous leaps out of the water. This is especially the case at night, when it is liable to be bewildered by the lights of fishing vessels. Instances have been known of men in boats being injured by these blind, panic-stricken flights. One had a leg pierced through, as by the thrust of a

rapier, and was pinned to the wood of a deckhouse. Another fared worse, for his jugular vein was ripped open, and he died before medical help could be found. It can be imagined what havoc this needlefish can cause with its fine-toothed jaws when it gets among a school of smaller fishes. There follows an orgy of greedy feeding. Its speed and weight make it, size for size, one of the most destructive raiders of the sea.

THE SACRED COD

Deep in the icy depths of the North Atlantic

Atlantic cod *(Gadus callarias)*

lives a fish whose popularity as a tasty food has remained undimmed for centuries. The **Atlantic cod** is so popular in Boston, for example, that the citizens of that city – sometimes called "The Land of the Bean and the Cod" – have enthroned a large cod on a wall of their state house. This famous fish is called "The Sacred Cod". The Atlantic cod has provided a hazardous living for generations of hardy fishermen in New England, Canada, Norway, England and Iceland who venture into the stormy Atlantic to drag their huge trawls through the beds of cod which live between ten and twenty fathoms below the surface. The Atlantic cod, which usually weighs between two and a half and twenty five pounds, has an astonishing number of brothers and sisters. One 75-pound cod laid nine million eggs during her lifetime. Even though the Atlantic cod is a favourite table fish, especially dried and salted before being cooked, many people remember their first encounter with the cod, in the form of health-giving but not so tasty cod liver oil!

FISH OF A SUNKEN CONTINENT

A mysterious sunken continent is said to lie beneath the waters off the coast of southwest Ireland, extending to the coast of Brittany. In these eerie depths swims a favourite fish of French housewives, the **European hake.**

This fish had a 500-year holiday from the hazards of being caught and eaten. During the Middle Ages, in 1404, the entire fleet of the hake-catching Spanish Basque fishermen was wiped out by a fierce storm, and it was not until about 1910 that this strong-toothed hunter of shrimp and smaller fish was again placed on European tables. The European hake, once classified not only with the cod, to which it is related, but with the pike as well, has very regular habits, and invariably stays all day long at the bottom of the ocean. But too rigid a schedule is not a good thing. The wise North Atlantic fishermen know exactly when the European hake will be on the ocean floor, and they have an easy job scooping them up by their wriggling thousands into the bellies of their huge hake trawls.

STRANGE JAWS

The name of the order to which the moonfish or **opah** belongs is Allotriognathi, a long Greek word meaning "strange jaws". It certainly is appropriate. The fish grows to a length of up to six feet, with a weight of several hundred pounds, and it has jaws to match. They are "protrusible". This means that, in the very act of opening its mouth to bite, its jaws are shot forward, the mouth being then rounded like an "o", the whole forming a kind of nozzle. Thus, this fish is capable of fastening

European hake *(Merluccius merluccius)*

Opah (*Lampris regius*)

cuttlefish of large size were found in it. Near Madeira the opah also dines on sea woodlice (isopods), which are plentiful there. Whatever its diet its flesh is said to have an excellent flavour, although it is never found in sufficient numbers to satisfy the demand of those who seek it.

on any victim which might have deemed itself just out of range. Squids and octopuses form the chief food of the opah, but it is fond of cuttlefish, too. This has been proved on opening an opah's stomach, when the horny indigestible beaks of no fewer than fifty-four

Mottled grouper (*Epinephelus fuscoguttatus*)

ONE OF THE FAMILY
A favourite of skin-divers, the groupers belong to an enormous family of perch-like fishes, numbering more than four hundred species in all, that thrive in tropical waters, and to a lesser extent in temperate waters, around the world, each wonderfully adapted to its own particular environment. The whole tribe seems to be bursting with vitality and robust good health, seeming to flourish in spite of every misfortune. One of the heavier-bodied, the **mottled grouper,** feeds on the swarms of small coastal fish that lurk in the shadow of wrecked ships, or dart among the great brown seaweeds and branching coral thickets, off the coast of Ceylon. Camouflaged by its irregular colouring and well-equipped with sharp teeth set in its great spreading mouth, it may even venture out among the schooling fish that follow the coastal currents, rich in food, down the slopes of the continental shelf to the edge of the abyss. Here, among countless others of its kind, it moves with confidence, as if the world were its oyster.

MORE DANGEROUS THAN SHARKS
"More dangerous than sharks", is the verdict of divers exploring the crevices and caverns of Australia's Great Barrier Reef. This is the Queensland grouper, or **giant barrier reef fish,** whose inquisitiveness is as insatiable as its terrific appetite. It has been known to stalk a shell-diver as a cat stalks a mouse, and to make a rush with the full impetus of its quarter-ton weight. Australian newspapers report salvage-divers being repeatedly attacked by groupers attracted by the shiny helmets. One fish took a helmet in its mouth and made off, of course dragging the wearer with it. The man was rescued in the nick of time. Brisbane Marine Officials say: "It is thought that the mysterious loss of some native pearl divers is due to Groupers". This great fish is most often found lurking in deep valleys or old wrecks on the sea floor. It has a cavernous mouth, and this has given rise to legends of skin-divers being swallowed alive. Fortunately

Giant barrier reef fish (*Promicrops lanceolatus*)

76

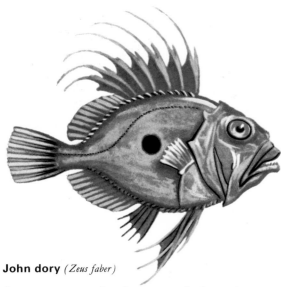

John dory *(Zeus faber)*

these are untrue, for the grouper's throat is not wide enough!

A SLIM STALKER

Seen head-on in the water, the **John dory** is almost invisible to the fish it is stalking – as though it were an oiled-paper cut-out standing on end. It advances slowly, making no whirl or ripple until within inches of the victim. At

Large-mouth bass *(Micropterus salmoides)*

this point any movement of its body would alarm an alert and agile fish, but the John dory does not move its body. Instead, its protrusible jaws not only open wide, but simultaneously jerk forward in a lightning-like thrust, and the small fish is taken by surprise. You may notice in the picture how the lower jaw projects. It is part of a mechanism which helps to make life easy. Yet the John dory is itself easy to catch because it lives at mid-water levels in busily-fished waters from the British Isles southwards into the Mediterranean. It is from this sea that Saint Peter is supposed to have taken a John dory and found a piece of money in its mouth. The very conspicuous black spot on the side of the fish is supposed to represent the mark of the Saint's thumb.

BATTLING FOR LIFE

Of all the world's fish, whether in fresh or salt water, none leads a more desperate existence than the North American **large-mouth bass.** From the first independent swim after hatching, the young bass has to battle furiously for its life. Eat or be eaten is the law in its slow-moving rivers and green-margined lakes. The mouth of the youngster grows wider almost daily, graduating from snails, worms, crayfish, tadpoles and mice to the fully-grown large-mouth of two to three feet long which can

Bluefish (*Pomatomus salatrix*)

engulf large frogs, rats, snakes, and even little ducklings unlucky enough to swim overhead. When he is guarding newly-hatched fry the male is ferocious enough to scare off even the largest enemies, except such a deadly foe as the otter. A more subtle enemy, against which he is powerless, is the tapeworm that attacks his reproductive organs, making him incapable of fertilising eggs. If it were not for these, and other exterminators, the large-mouth bass would surely depopulate vast stretches of America's inland waters.

There are two kinds of fishes known as basses and although fairly closely related they belong to separate families. There are the sea basses and the freshwater basses of which the large-mouth bass is one of several species. The freshwater basses belong to the family known as the sunfishes. There is a sunfish living in the sea. The freshwater sunfishes have received their name because they react very quickly to sunshine. When the sun is shining they disperse and go about their original occupations but when a cloud obscures the sun they bunch together as though something had alarmed them.

The large-mouth bass does not behave in this way but it is included in the same family because its anatomy is like that of the typical sunfish. In fact the large-mouth bass behaves like a typical hunter. Although it will eat almost anything living that comes its way, its main food is other fishes and to catch these it lurks among the roots of water plants or between stones, and from its hide-out pounces on its prey as it passes.

As so often happens with a species that is highly predatory, the large-mouth bass is particularly belligerent towards others of its own species. One result of this is to keep the individual fishes spaced out, but the belligerence is especially marked during the breeding season. The male bass builds his nest and defends it and the territory immediately around it against all other males. Fights along the borders between the territories are quite common. However, should a female enter the territory he meets her with raised fins and after a brief courtship the two begin to circle inside the nest, she laying a few eggs at a time and he fertilising them. But the moment she has finished laying he drives her out.

Several females may lay in one nest, which may in the end contain up to 10,000 eggs.

DRIVEN BY BLOOD-LUST

The bloodthirsty habits of the **bluefish** can only be compared with those of the South American piranha. It lives in tropical and temperate Atlantic waters, and when raiding a shoal of menhaden or other herring-type fish for food, it continues its massacre long after its appetite has been glutted. Vivid reports tell of the effect of mass attacks on a vast concourse of fleeing menhaden. For miles around the sea is carpeted with bloody fragments and mutilated skeletons. In fact the bluefish seems to go crazy when it smells blood, and kills for the sake of killing. It is this craving which helps anglers to attract it to their hooks. They first of all "bait" the sea with chopped-up fish and fish-blood, which they are sure will bring the bluefish in from afar. A first-class fighting fish, weighing up to twenty-seven pounds, it is voted "good sport and good eating", and the demand is nearly always greater than the supply. Inshore, young bluefish are common, being known as "tailors" or "snappers".

The bluefish is a quite ordinary looking fish but the description sometimes given it, of the most ferocious cold-blooded murderer of the fish world, is not unjustified. It has also been described as an animated chopping machine. It has been estimated that 1,000,000 bluefish operate in this wholesale fashion for 120 days each summer in the waters off the Atlantic coasts of the United States. When it is realized that on each of these days they destroy ten times their own number of other fishes we have a picture of mortality among sea fishes reaching astronomical proportions. If this does nothing else it helps us to appreciate the truly tremendous numbers of fishes in the sea since the prey species of the bluefish can sustain each year these very high casualties, from this one cause alone, without showing signs of exhaustion of their own numbers.

THE KILLER LOG

As motionless as a log, the **northern pike** waits for an unsuspecting swimmer to pass by. When that moment arrives, the "pike of wood" suddenly becomes a ferocious killer. Pouncing on its catch, the sharp and savage teeth in that shovel-snout seize and devour the victim. The pike will lie in wait for almost anything that lives in a stream or lake : worms, frogs, trout, even younger pike. In our eyes, its cruellest "waiting game" is for the ducklings that stray away from their mother's watchful eye. It need only seize one tiny, webbed foot for the bird's end to be assured. The northern pike is a prowler of many freshwater streams in North America, as well as in the rivers of Europe and northern Asia. Like all true savages, it flourishes only in the wild, far from man's cities. If man and his ways do not press too close, however, the killer may live to a ripe old age of fifteen years. The old rogue then may reach a length of forty-five inches, and weigh as much as thirty-five pounds.

THE "LEAF" WITH A VACUUM CLEANER

When is a leaf not a leaf? Natives of South America's Amazon River basin can tell you that a "leaf", with its "stem", often seen floating sluggishly downstream is really the voracious three-inch **leaf fish** which eats its own weight in smaller fish every day. This

◄ **Northern pike** (*Esox lucius*)

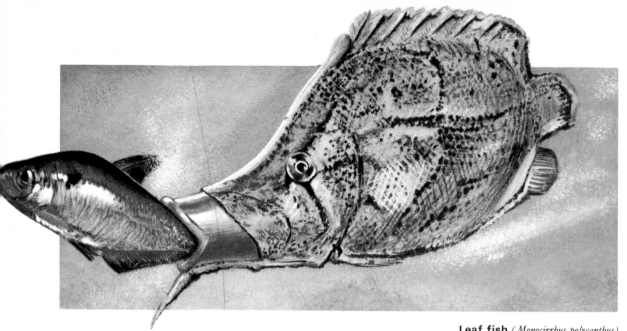

fantastic fish does not resemble merely one leaf. It not only mimics the various leaves of its home waters by folding or expanding its saw-toothed fin edges, but its colour ranges from pale grey or tan to black, as do the fallen leaves found floating on the water in which it lives. Its resemblance to a leaf is enhanced by a fleshy barbel on its chin which looks like a stem as the fish drifts slowly and imperceptibly towards its prey. When close enough to its prey, the leaf fish shoots out its mouth to form a tube and sucks in the smaller victim with the efficiency of a vacuum cleaner.

MURDER IN THE BASEMENT

Burrowed in the sandy bottom of the sea, the **greater weeverfish** lies motionless, its spiny dorsal fin swaying slightly in the slow wash of the current, like a Japanese fan. Attracted by the fluttering motion of this fan, a fish questions it gently with its protruding mouth – and receiving the deadly answer, floats like a corpse just off the sea-bed, paralysed by the poisonous spines. Delicately, at leisure, the dapper little poisoner consumes its meal. A small elongated fish, no more than eighteen inches long, the greater weeverfish is a deep-

Greater weeverfish *(Trachinus draco)*

water species, ranging from the Baltic to the Black Sea. Its cousins, the lesser weevers, that lack black stripes around the body, are a menace to waders in shallow waters along the coasts of Europe and north-west Africa; another weever has established a flourishing colony along the coast of Chile. But the whole family has the same light touch, the same murderous end.

The Romans knew of the evil properties of the weeverfish and in other European countries at all times their dangerous character has been recognised. In England it has been marked by giving this fish the vernacular name of sea dragon. Not only are they aggressive when living but they are dangerous to handle when in a net, and even dead specimens handled imprudently can cause extreme pain. It is very easy, and it not infrequently happens with venomous species of animals, to overstate the danger and to exaggerate the consequences arising from their venom. So far as the weeverfish is concerned we have to be content with repeating what other people have said on this point. They talk of excruciating agony as the first symptom of being stung by a weeverfish, and some reports speak of this agony as so great that people have acted as if they were insane. Even if these stories are not literally true, and there is no reason at the moment to doubt that they are true, they would at least symbolize the dangers that could arise from handling a weeverfish, and if they serve as a warning then there is some point to them. It should perhaps be pointed out that there are 30,000 different kinds of fishes in the world and of these less than 100 present dangers of this kind to human beings. There may be others that can cause discomfort in some form or another but the number capable of dispensing a really painful or fatal venom is very limited.

THE FISH WITH ITS OWN BAIT

It is an odd notion that a fish should have its own worm-like bait to lure other fish to their doom, but a number of fishes are so equipped. One is the **electric stargazer**. This foot-long fish has a worm-shaped lure springing from its mouth which allows it to catch its food without undue effort. Wallowing on the Eastern Atlantic or Mediterranean sea-bed, it waits for its dinner to approach. When it sees a nice crustacean, it simply waves its bait. The hapless victim, deceived into biting what looks like an appetizing worm, is gathered into the electric

stargazer's big mouth after being paralysed by a powerful 50-volt shock from two electrical cells behind the electric stargazer's eyes. It is called a "stargazer" because it spends most of its time buried in mud or sand, with only its eyes and part of its fringed mouth protruding toward the stars. The electric stargazer can not only produce powerful electric shocks, but has two large poison spines above its fins, and these have been known to kill a man with their deadly venom.

THE TAIL-WALKER

With the sea foaming about its powerful shoulders and its great sail slanted before the wind, the **Pacific sailfish** drifts before the wind like a Chinese junk. Suddenly the sky darkens, the breeze freshens, and the sailfish lowers its sail into the groove along the top of

Electric stargazer (*Uranoscopus scaber*)

81

Pacific sailfish (*Istiophorus orientalis*)

its back and plunges below the surface. Several hours later, it sights a school of smaller fishes and, overtaking them, stuns and maims its prey with sideways strokes of its long bill, the sea boiling around the twelve-foot sailfish as the frantic school seeks to escape. Its own flesh is oily and it is not a favourite food fish but is highly prized as a game-fish by sports fishermen. Usually caught by trolling in deep water, when hooked it leaps, twists and literally seems to walk on its tail on the water, as it strives to throw the hook. Thrashing in the troubled air above the calm ocean, the small scales embedded in its skin like silver coins, its highly-coloured sail shining in the sunlight, it is one of the most magnificent fish in the Indo-Pacific Ocean. If it occasionally spears a fish this is accidental.

IN THE NAVAL TRADITION

During the early critical months following the entry of the United States into the Second World War, the American submarine, "USS Wahoo", racked up one of the all-time records for enemy sinkings and was one of the few ships, below or above the surface, that was able to wage aggressive war against the enemy. Until sunk in 1942, the "Wahoo" was a mainstay of the United States fleet based at Pearl Harbour in the Hawaiian Islands. In this same tradition of service, few fish have proven so useful to man as the **wahoo mackerel,** after which the famous submarine was named. Easily recognized by its deeply-forked tail and the wavy bands on the sides of its silvery torpedo-shaped body, it is the heavy-weight of the Mackerel family,

Wahoo mackerel *(Acanthocybium solandri)*

sometimes tipping the scales at more than 120 pounds. Related to the Spanish mackerel, another fast-moving tuna type, it is considered to be one of the world's best food fishes and has a high commercial value.

BETWEEN THE TIDES

Along the margins of the seas – in the tidal pools, the swaying eel-grass and the kelp beds – swim many kinds of carnivorous little fish that feed on small animals and fish larvae living between the tides. Difficult to identify, yet seen by everyone who has walked the beaches, these, to most people, anonymous little fish are members of the blenny family. Found in all tropical or temperate seas, in bays and inlets, in brackish or salt water, these are the fish of the tide-pools, oyster-beds and mud flats. Like the **fringehead blenny,** which lives among the rocks and stones of the shallow waters of the Mediterranean, some are scaleless with handsome, fleshy filaments or fringes on top of their heads; others are scaled and darkly mottled to blend with the reddish kelp or the eel-grass. A sea-bed dweller, the fringehead blenny is a necessary rung in the ladder of life.

SEA-ROVER

Swiftest of fishes in the ocean, the **swordfish** hurtles through the sea at well over thirty miles an hour, its powerful broad sword cleaving the foaming water like the sharp prow of a ship, its sleek flanks shedding the sea smoothly backward, while its strong tail acts as a powerful

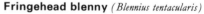

Fringehead blenny *(Blennius tentacularis)*

rudder. Although it often basks at the surface and is not easily disturbed, it turns furiously on pursuers when wounded, rushing through the water at top speed, and is capable of driving its sword through the planking of small ships. A huge fish, growing as long as fifteen feet and weighing as much as one thousand pounds, it is often taken by sports fishermen with a line but is hunted commercially with the harpoon. Feeding on smaller fish, which it stuns with sideways blows of its "beak", it is itself hunted in all the world's oceans – as far north as the Barents Sea. Wandering round the world's watery surface, the swordfish is the last of the sea-rovers. When a swordfish drives its beak into the timbers of a ship this can be counted as accidental, and not as a deliberate attack. It must be accidental, also, when it spears a small fish.

TORPEDO!

Life at sea holds few terrors for the merchant seaman equal to the shrill clanging of the ship's alarm and the cry – "Torpedo"! Beneath the surface of the ocean, the diver feels a similar cold thrill of fear when confronted by the torpedo-shaped outline of the **great barracuda.** Suspended ominously in the clear water, it does

not stalk its prey but will attack anything that makes erratic movements – such as a wounded fish. Hunting alone or in packs, it is the most dangerous of its kind as well as the largest – it sometimes reaches a length of twelve feet, although six feet is more usual. Unlike a shark, it makes a single attack that leaves a clean wound with no jagged edges, but its jutting jaw with its fang-like teeth is capable of severing an arm. Arrowing through the water towards its target, impelled by the relentless drive of its hunger, the great barracuda is probably the most deadly submarine danger in the ocean.

It used to be said that sharks sever a man's limb in one bite. In recent years, there has been a great deal of research into the ways and habits of sharks, largely in an endeavour to devise methods of preventing attacks by sharks near bathing beaches. At the same time several books have been published giving their authors' researches into the case histories of people that have been injured by sharks. As a result of these researches it seems highly unlikely that a shark ever severs a limb, and that when a limb is found in a shark's stomach it is because the shark has come across a corpse in a state of decomposition so that the limb has come away naturally from the rest of the body.

Swordfish (*Xiphias gladius*)

Great barracuda (*Sphyraena barracuda*)

Attack by the great barracuda seems to be as vicious and as dangerous as that of any shark, and very often it is a matter for doubt whether the person who has been injured in the sea has been attacked by a shark or a barracuda. It does seem, however, that a large barracuda can in fact sever a limb with one snap of the jaws. Another feature of barracuda attack, which makes it a greater menace than attack by shark is that it may take place in much shallower water.

All this must sound very frightening, and there is no question that the barracuda must be treated with the greatest possible respect. Nevertheless, compared with the number of

people that go bathing or skin-diving, barracuda attacks are much less frequent than attacks by sharks, and like shark attacks they occur only in the warmer waters.

THE FISH FACTORY

The most repulsive fish in the ocean, the **monkfish** spends its time lying on the mud of the sea floor, fishing. Camouflaged against its background, like a hunter in a duck-blind, it is one of the world's most successful anglers. An odd shaped creature – its cavernous mouth is nearly as wide as its head – it may grow to more than four feet in length and weigh as much as seventy pounds. Its fishing rod is modified from the first of its six dorsal fin spines. This it waves back and forth above its mouth, a fold of loose flesh at the tip acting as a lure. Anything that moves is fair prey – seabirds, small sharks, crabs, fishes. A veritable fish factory, it pays the penalty of success, for, in spite of its repulsive appearance, its flesh is excellent and the monkfish is widely-marketed throughout Europe and Asia. In Britain, at least, this ugly-looking fish is never seen in a fishmonger's shop until it has been skinned and gutted and its flesh cut up into fish steaks. And even then it is given fancy names, so that people buying it for the table do not know that they are eating such an unpleasant-looking fish.

Monkfish or angler-fish (*Lophius piscatorius*)

85

THE FRIENDLY KILLER

The name **dolphin** is given to a fish and also to a mammal, and this can be confusing; but the adult "fish" can be easily recognised by its long continuous fin and forked tail – particularly by its friend, the sailor. But to other and smaller fish, the dolphin is a fast-moving killer that hunts at speeds up to thirty-seven knots. Its appetite is enormous, and it feeds on a variety of fishes and invertebrates; thirty-two different species of fishes representing nineteen families have been found in the stomachs of the Atlantic dolphin! Attracted by the lights of ships, it ventures out by night much more frequently than the mammal, and its brilliant hues reflect in the moonlight. It grows rapidly but its life-span is very short; no more than two to three years.

Dolphin (Fish) *(Coryphaena hippurus)*

European common toad *(Bufo bufo)*

A good indication of how quickly dolphins grow has been obtained from the results of keeping 52 of them in the Marine Studios in Florida. Each of these was at most 18 inches long and weighed $1\frac{1}{2}$ pounds when first introduced into the tank in late August. Because of their enormous appetites these fishes were fed three times a day. In December of the same year one of them leapt out of the tank and was found to measure 45 inches long and to weigh nearly 25 pounds.

SLOW BODY, FAST TONGUE

Although it has a clumsy body and a slow-motion crawl, the European **common toad** is an expert raider of harmful insects and slugs. Its lazy movements are compensated for by a tongue that can flick out and in again with lightning speed. In catching an insect it is, at first, motionless, watching with apparently unseeing eyes, only a slight tilt of the head showing how attentive it is. It waits for the insect to move into a convenient position. Then the huge mouth flies open, and out shoots the tongue before the insect can beat a wing. You see this stage in the picture. The tongue-tip is wrapped round the victim, which is about to be swallowed alive. The European common toad can also tackle the worms wriggling frantically, and other crawlers. The toad holds them tightly between horny lips and crams them gradually into its cavernous mouth with curiously "human" movements of its hands. This toad has been known to live thirty-six years.

European common frog (*Rana temporaria*)

HARDY ANNUAL

Not only common in Europe, but in temperate areas of Asia, even to Japan, this frog is wonderfully hardy. Where there is herbage to shelter in, and water for the breeding season, it finds food in the shape of slugs, snails, worms and insects, which it captures by shooting out its long tongue, with its sticky tip, and drawing it back again with the victim attached. It does this with such lightning speed that a human eye cannot detect the movement. One instant an insect is there, then it is not! Not only the frog, but the tadpoles that come from the eggs have many enemies. But there are so many eggs, and so many tadpoles, that the frog population never seems to decrease, as the result of predation, only as the result of a decrease in the number of ponds. In winter the **common frog** hibernates, at the bottom of a muddy pond or in the ground, sometimes many together. In spring, the frogs emerge and the females lay the eggs which we find in masses in still water.

CANNIBAL IN FANCY DRESS

The continent of South America has produced some queer frogs but none is more extraordinary than this horned cannibal in harlequin dress. **Bell's horned frog** grows to four to five inches long and haunts the streams and swamps of Argentina, Paraguay and Uruguay. Squatting on its haunches, as still as death, it is practically invisible against the variegated greens, and the lights and shades of its background. One would think it asleep or incapable of movement, but let any other creature, frog, lizard or large insect, make the slightest move

within reach of it, and it is doomed. Quick as a flash Bell's horned frog pounces. Dagger-sharp teeth crush the head of the victim, which is then stuffed into the enormous mouth and swallowed by degrees. The picture shows a South American bull frog, despite its size, caught in this way. The stomach of this cannibal is capable of great distension to deal with a giant meal, yet a day or two may pass before the bull frog is finally digested.

Because it is so ready to attack, even an animal many times its own size, this horned frog is apt to be surrounded by strange beliefs and exaggerated stories. In the Argentine, for example, it is said that the frog will bite the lip of a horse grazing where it is squatting and that the horse will die from the bite. As usual, with such beliefs, it is impossible to come across authentic records of this having taken place. Since the frog has no poison in its mouth the chances are that its bite would not be lethal to a horse. It is, on the other hand, conceivable that a horse may sometimes be bitten in this way. It is even possible that at some time or another a horse has been bitten and has subsequently died, and it may even have died from the wound having become septic from other causes. If this happened once it would be enough for the belief to become founded, and the human love of a spectacular story would be sufficient to perpetuate the belief.

Bell's horned frog (*Ceratophrys cornuta*)

Itannia horned frog (*Ceratophrys dorsata*)

ANOTHER CANNIBAL

Lying half-buried in the undergrowth on the floor of a South American forest with only its evil little eyes moving as it keeps watch, the ferocious **Itannia horned frog** waits for some unsuspecting victim. Cunningly dazzle-camouflaged in different coloured stripes so that, like a warship, its mass and outline is obscured, it lurks unseen until its chosen prey, some invertebrate or amphibian, is close enough. Then it attacks. Leaping out of its foxhole it jumps through the air to seize its next meal in its wide powerful jaws. This frog is peculiar in possessing long pointed teeth from a very early age, and humans have to treat it carefully if they want to avoid a nasty bite as the frog struggles to escape. Unbelievably greedy, it has been known to eat its own weight of food in one day. As the Itannia horned frog is also a cannibal the day's diet may have included some of its own family and this probably explains why this sort of frog is not found in greater numbers.

A CAT-EYED FROG

Its wide mouth and strong jaws indicate that the **Asiatic horned frog** is not the gentlest of creatures, and it has been suggested that these features indicate that it is cannibalistic, and that it is able to eat larger prey than the beetles and small invertebrate victims of most frogs. Hunting mainly at night, it has eyes with vertical pupils, like those of a cat. These eyes, combined with the "horns" from which it gets its name, one above each eyelid and one at the end of its nose, give it the baleful appearance of some primaeval monster. Tadpoles of this frog have wide "umbrella mouths", the lips growing wide apart, forming a sort of funnel into which they scoop their food. Another, nearly-related species living in Malaya produces tadpoles that float upright in the water as if their peculiarly large mouths were acting as floats, keeping the tadpoles just below the surface of the water. Inside the wide lips are rows of teeth which comb the leaves of passing water plants, scraping off the microscopic plant and animal life which form the tadpoles' food.

BETTER THAN SAVING CERTIFICATES

How comes it that the giant South American **marine toad** is saving millions of pounds a year in Australia? It is a wonderful story. In its native haunts it may be as much as eight or nine inches long, and weigh up to 3 lbs. It eats everything spiny, furry, feathered or smooth-skinned it sees moving within striking distance. But especially, and this is the point of the story, it eats beetles! Now look at Queensland, Australia, where cultivation of the sugar cane is a vital, valuable industry. Some years ago these sugar crops were threatened with destruction by the grey-backed cane beetle. So the marine toad was imported from South America to eat up the beetles. The big question was: would the marine toad survive in a foreign land? It has more than survived. It simply swarms there. Not only is it protected by virulent poison-glands in its neck which kill would-be killers, but the female lays batches of up to 35,000 eggs a year – each one a potential death threat to beetles. What is more, this toad has been introduced into Haiti, Puerto Rico, Guan, Hawaii and the Solomon Islands, and other sugar-raising countries.

Asiatic horned frog (*Megophrys nasuta*)

KING JUMPER

Most of us have heard of Mark Twain's "Celebrated Jumping Frog". Actually it was just an ordinary **American bullfrog,** able to leap nearly ten times its own length. More interesting is how it uses its jumping powers in feeding. It sits at the edge of a lake or swamp, perhaps surrounded by such tempting morsels as young water birds, baby turtles or insects. So long as they stand still, the frog is unable to see them. Only when they move, however slightly, does it flash into action, hurling itself up or forward like a bullet. Its tongue curls round the victim, its hands cram it into its gaping mouth, all in mid-air, and the frog settles softly down on its enormous thighs, ready for the next unwary animal to move. Its leaps are so well-timed that it can even catch swallows on the wing when they swoop low over water. In each colony the strongest American bullfrog is king. It will not let others jump for food until its own stomach is full. However, this New World giant, measuring some eight inches, is still out-jumped by its tiny one-inch cousin, the **cricket frog,** which can leap a distance thirty-six times its own length, which is just under two inches.

For a long time there has been much discussion about how a frog uses its tongue to catch insects and other prey in the air. Most people were content to say it catches them with its sticky tongue. Then, about twenty years ago, high-speed photographs showed the end of the tongue wrapped round an insect.

The tongue, when not in action, is folded in the floor of the mouth at the front. As the frog leaps at its prey the mouth opens and at the

1. American bullfrog (*Rana catesbeiana*)

2. Cricket frog (*Acris crepitans*)

same time a set of small muscles come into play shooting the tongue forward. The outer half of the tongue contains no muscles fibres but is so elastic that the force with which it is ejected causes it to stretch to two or three times its length. This whips round the insect and holds it just long enough to be drawn back into the frog's mouth.

The time taken for the tongue to be shot out is a twentieth of a second. The time for it to be pulled in again is even less. The speed is too great for the eye to follow. Only the electronic flash with synchronized camera could give the answer. Even so, a twentieth of a second is sufficient time for an insect to wriggle free, and if the bullfrog, or any other frog, is not to waste energy in fruitless leaps something more is needed. This is supplied by its sticky saliva, and also by very minute roughnesses on the tongue which help it to grip.

Marine toad (*Bufo marinus*)

THE LARGEST OF ALL FROGS

With a long leap one of nature's shyest creatures dives into the water and wriggles out of sight under a thick layer of mud just as a scoop-net swishes empty a few scant inches behind it. Then, slowly, it raises its head from under its dark cover and watches the shadow of a boat gliding silently away. The **goliath frog** has once more escaped its would-be captors. In Africa, the Congolese hunt it for its thigh bones, believing that they possess a magic power to bring good luck. In fact, they value this frog so highly that they refuse to sell it – dead or alive – to animal dealers and zoos despite the excellent prices offered. The goliath frog, as its name implies, is the largest known frog in existence, measuring up to ten inches in length. It is believed that it grows even larger. However, the big ones always seem to get away.

Because so few specimens have reached the learned institutions we know little more about the goliath frog than its outward appearance and its anatomy. There was a live frog that reached the Natural History Museum in Paris in 1950. The pygmy hunters of West Africa shoot the frog with bow and arrow. This one had been wounded by pygmies but was rescued and lived several weeks in a vivarium. The man who took it to Paris reported that the goliath frog feeds mainly on fish. But there has been a specimen in the Natural History Museum, in

Goliath frog (*Gigantorana goliath*) compared in size to common frog (bottom right)

Smoky jungle frog (*Leptodactylus pentadactylus*)

London for the past sixty years. This is stuffed and mounted in a show case in the Museum's galleries. It is shown in a squatting position with its large mouth slightly agape and with the hindquarters and tail of a medium-sized rat protruding from its mouth. At the time that the specimen was received by the Museum inquiries were made, by correspondence and by word of mouth, of those with experience of West Africa, and as a result of these there is every reason to believe that rats form at least part of the goliath frog's diet.

SNAKE-SWALLOWING FROG

Unbelievable but true, this cold-blooded 8-inch monster, though weighing only a pound, swallows snakes, lizards, bats, birds – in fact any living thing that will go through its gin-trap jaws. As a ferocious killer the **smoky jungle frog** of Panama has few equals. It sits as still as a stone, its glazed globular eyes bulging, waiting for a potential meal to move. Then, at the least sign of life, out flashes its whiplash tongue, faster than the human eye can follow, and the victim is jerked into the frog's cavernous mouth. Should a lizard be too big to swallow, Smoky will seize it with its enormously strong forearms and cram the lizard's head forcibly into its mouth. Hind legs may kick, and tail squirm, but the lizard is soon suffocated and engulfed. The picture shows Smoky enjoying a snake three feet long. It will have to wait until its digestive juices dissolve the head and neck before it can take in the next instalment, but the longer the meal lasts the better – from the frog's point-of-view!

Japanese giant salamander
(Megalobatrachus japonicus)

Chinese salamander *(Megalobatrachus davidianus)*

FLAT-HEAD

Largest of the weird race of salamanders, the
Japanese giant salamander may grow to a
length of five feet. It remains during the day
curled round convenient rocks in the beds of
streams. At night it cruises like a submarine in
search of worms, crustaceans, fish or frogs –
and newts, which are a special delicacy. In
August and September the female lays very
tiny eggs, so that when the young hatch out
they are only about an inch long. Yet they are
remarkable miniature replicas of their parents,
except for small differences, amongst which is
the possession of rudimentary fins. At one
time the Japanese valued their giant salamander
as a tasty food and as having medicinal properties, but it is getting scarce now, and is
mainly caught for exhibition in zoos. In
aquarium tanks it becomes sluggish and may
remain immobile for hours.

A CHINESE WATER-DRAGON

Although regarded as a lizard in the time of
Confucius, the large **Chinese salamander** is
not a reptile but an amphibian. Living in
remote Western Central China, it is seldom
seen, for it dwells in streams, sometimes no
more than a foot wide and covered in by
grasses and reeds. In the daytime this salamander stays underwater, save for periodic
visits to the surface for air. Slow-moving and
stoutly-built, it ventures onto land only at
night to search for worms, crustaceans and
frogs. A snapping movement of its jaws and

a swift sideways movement of its head indicate that this warty waddler has made another kill. To rest from the night's work it returns to the stream and curls its long body round a convenient stem in the water. Three and a half feet long when full-grown, it begins life as an extremely tiny egg.

SLIMY HUNTER

A fisherman, along one of the rivers of the South Appalachian region of the United States, senses a bite and immediately reels in his line. There, dangling from his hook, is a grotesque-looking foot-long salamander staring him menacingly in the eye. Rather than risk touching the feared **hellbender**, which he believes to be poisonous and dangerous, the terrified man cuts his line, and casts the slimy, though quite harmless, creature back into its muddy home. In its usual manner, the salamander sluggishly swims away, and resumes its normal occupation, crawling awkwardly about the mud on its stubby, crocodile-like legs, searching for crayfish or aquatic insects. Occasionally it will venture on land, where it may remain for 24 hours at a time, to hunt earthworms, its flattened head covered with wart-like bumps, and its smooth skin wrinkled into folds, making it look a rather bizarre creature waddling about the underbrush.

The hellbender feeds mainly at night and depends on its sense of smell, aided by touch to locate its prey.

Warty newt *(Triturus cristatus)*

QUICK-CHANGE ARTIST

Almost as easily as a man can slip out of his shirt, the **warty newt** can take off its own outer layer of skin. Indeed, the simile is almost completed by the sight of this crested salamander pushing off the old skin with its fingers, but it is a trifle spoiled by the time it wraps up the old skin and neatly pops it into its mouth. Unlike some amphibians, the warty newt's skin does not stretch as it grows, so it simply grows a new layer and sheds the old skin from time to time until it has attained its full six-inch length. This shy creature is the largest of the European newts and except

Hellbender *(Cryptobranchus alleganiensis)*

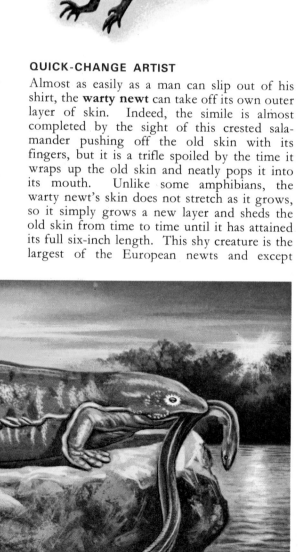

Pacific giant salamander
(Dicamptodon ensatus)

AN EVOLUTIONARY CORNER

Even in the strange twilight world of the amphibians, the **two-toed amphiuma,** known locally as a "conger eel", seems a curious specimen. Unlike its namesake, the large seven-foot marine eel, which is a fish, the salamander "eel" rarely reaches three feet in length, and lives in the muddy inland streams and rivers that vein the eastern half of the North American continent. Like most salamanders, it is nocturnal, emerging only at night to forage for food, attacking fish, water beetles, and crustaceans, and hiding by day among the matted water weeds. Like the true eel, which it so closely resembles, it has a vicious bite and defends itself fiercely. Indeed, were it not for the small useless legs that cling to its flowing elongate body, it would be difficult to believe that this is an amphibian. The "conger eel" is a watery renegade, who having failed to turn the evolutionary corner, now finds itself slipping backwards to resemble superficially the fishes, from which its ancestors originally sprang.

Two-toed amphiuma *(Amphiuma means)*

during the breeding season lives on land, in central or northern Europe, including Britain. It hides under rocks, leaving them only to forage for insects and worms. The plume-like crest of the warty newt's back has made it a favourite of juvenile pet collectors.

SING FOR YOUR SUPPER

Although most salamanders are voiceless, the **Pacific giant salamander,** which lives in the damp forests from northern California to British Columbia, has the ability to make a noise that is variously described as a bark, scream, or low-pitched rattling. Despite its ungainly build, it climbs well and can be found on bushes and sloping tree trunks, hunting for snails, slugs, worms, beetles, even other salamanders, small snakes and mammals, such as shrews and mice. Growing to nearly a foot in length, it eats anything of suitable size it can catch. Nocturnal, like all salamanders, it hides during the day under the damp mat of forest leaves, among loose pebbles near spring seepage, or following crevices in stone outcroppings to a depth of twenty feet. Sensitive to sunlight, it may sometimes be seen by day in the filtered gloom of the forest trees, but prefers to search for its supper when the sun goes down. Largest of the land-frequenting salamanders, it is one of the most successful, never going to bed hungry.

ILLEGAL GUILT

*Jeffrey Ashford titles available from
Severn House Large Print*

Deadly Corruption
Evidentially Guilty
Fair Exchange is Robbery
A Truthful Injustice